GETTING STARTED GUIDE 1

Inspire Maths consultant and author
Dr Fong Ho Kheong

Rebecca Holland   Julie Mitchell   Bernie Westacott

OXFORD
UNIVERSITY PRESS

OXFORD
UNIVERSITY PRESS

Great Clarendon Street, Oxford, OX2 6DP, United Kingdom

Oxford University Press is a department of the University of Oxford.

It furthers the University's objective of excellence in research, scholarship, and education by publishing worldwide. Oxford is a registered trade mark of Oxford University Press in the UK and in certain other countries.

ISBN 9780198428725

10 9 8 7 6 5 4 3 2 1

Typeset by Q2A Media

Paper used in the production of this book is a natural, recyclable product made from wood grown in sustainable forests.

The manufacturing process conforms to the environmental regulations of the country of origin.

Printed in Great Britain by Ashford Colour Press

Acknowledgements

Written by Rebecca Holland and Julie Mitchell

With thanks to Sue Lowndes

The following are © Marshall Cavendish Education Pte Ltd and reproduced with kind permission: Inspire Maths Pupil Textbook 1A pp. 13, 20, 28, 61, 89, 109; Inspire Maths Pupil Textbook 1B pp. 31, 37, 83, 123; Inspire Maths Practice Book 1B pp. 63, 71; Inspire Maths Practice Book 1D p. 69; Inspire Maths Teacher's Guide 1A p. 163; Inspire Maths Teacher's Guide 1B p. 252; Inspire Maths Assessment Book 1 pp. 15, 75, 108; Inspire Maths Pupil Textbook 2A pp. 10, 12; Inspire Maths Teacher's Guide 3A pp. 63, 231; Inspire Maths Pupil Textbook 4B pp. 28, 40; Inspire Maths Teacher's Guide 4B p. 180; Inspire Maths Pupil Textbook 5A p. 71

Wentworth case study p. 13 © 2017 Westminster Publications

Photographs by Scissor Paper Stone, except: pp. 4, 5, 40, 41, 71: Oxford University Press; p. 8: Marshall Cavendish Education Pte Ltd; p. 16: St Paul's CE Primary School, Sunderland; p. 21: Lady Joanna Thornhill Endowed Primary School

Cover artwork by Daron Parton

We have tried to contact all copyright holders, but should there be any errors or omissions, we will be pleased to rectify them at the earliest opportunity.

With special thanks to: Harriers Banbury Academy, Banbury; Lady Joanna Thornhill Endowed Primary School, Ashford; Moreland Primary School, Islington; St Joseph's Roman Catholic Primary School, Darwen; St Paul's CE Primary School, Sunderland; Wentworth Primary School, Dartford; Westminster Publications

The authors and publisher would like to thank all schools and individuals who have helped to trial and review Inspire Maths resources.

www.oxfordprimary.co.uk/inspiremaths

Contents

Introduction to the Getting Started Guide

Welcome to the *Inspire Maths* Getting Started Guide. This guide has been written especially for UK primary school teachers to support you in successfully delivering the *Inspire Maths* programme. It is designed to equip you with a deep understanding of the *Inspire Maths* approach and the practical tools for successfully implementing *Inspire Maths*, helping to raise standards in the teaching and learning of mathematics.

The Guide starts with a **Proof of impact and research base** section, explaining the programme's positive results both in Singapore schools and internationally. We outline the research and trialling that have been carried out and embedded to create a world-class textbook. Since the publication of *Inspire Maths* in 2015 in the UK, an independent report by the University of Oxford has attested to the positive impact that *Inspire Maths* has had in schools, and we share the results of this report with you. This section also draws on the experience of UK schools that have been using *Inspire Maths* over the past few years. Teachers

describe the impact they have experienced from teaching with the programme, how they have seen a rise in their children's mathematical ability, and also how they have witnessed an increase in their children's confidence and enjoyment of mathematics. Finally, teachers give testimony to how using *Inspire Maths* has dramatically improved planning, teaching and assessment in their classrooms and their own confidence in teaching mathematics.

The section on **High achievement in mathematics and the importance of high-quality textbooks** looks at the research and design behind high-quality textbooks, why they are important, and how the features of *Inspire Maths* demonstrate its position as a high-quality textbook. We appreciate that it is important for you to understand how high-quality textbooks can be used to support a mastery approach in the classroom, and this section will show you the benefits of using *Inspire Maths* as your textbook programme.

The **Pace, progression and fidelity** section gives teachers guidance on pace, and demonstrates the step-by-step progression through a specific concept. It shows how *Inspire Maths* uses a highly-scaffolded learning framework that builds and consolidates knowledge to reach deep understanding. References to the medium-term planning charts and learning objectives will help you to plan and understand the time that needs to be spent on a topic. This section also explains how to use the Pupil Textbooks, Practice Books and Assessment Books together, in order

to consolidate and apply understanding. This guidance will help you to prepare your year's teaching, by understanding your starting point and where you are aiming for by the end of the academic year.

The **How to teach with *Inspire Maths*** section is your practical guide through all the teaching and learning material, demonstrating how the theoretical approach fits with the practical work in the classroom. It outlines the *Inspire Maths* approach, before giving specific examples of how to teach with the different elements of the programme. It also offers support and suggestions for struggling learners and quick graspers, same-day intervention and using the assessments.

Guidance on how the 'National curriculum in England: mathematics programmes of study' relates to *Inspire Maths*, and how to ensure that you teach all the Key Stage requirements, is covered in the **How does *Inspire Maths* relate to the National Curriculum?** section. This highly-practical section has examples from *Inspire Maths* I–6, to demonstrate how you can teach with *Inspire Maths* and be confident about covering all of the National Curriculum objectives by the end of Key Stages I and 2.

Finally, the **Further support for successful implementation** section directs you to the wealth of extra resources available on *Inspire Maths Online*. This includes videos, mixed-age planning guidance, interactive whiteboard toolkits, assessment trackers and beginning-, middle- and end-of-year assessments, which match age-related National Curriculum expectations.

We hope that you find this Getting Started Guide a useful and practical support to implement *Inspire Maths* successfully in your classroom.

Teaching with *Inspire Maths*

This chart demonstrates how *Inspire Maths* resources work together to support teachers in delivering the primary 'National curriculum in England: mathematics programmes of study'. To ensure that sufficient time is spent focusing in depth on fundamental concepts, the levels of *Inspire Maths* may cross over year borders. Moving at the right pace for your children ensures you spend the necessary time to develop and embed skills and understanding. By following the programme, including the Additional Activities available online, you can be confident that all relevant curriculum objectives will be covered by the end of each Key Stage.

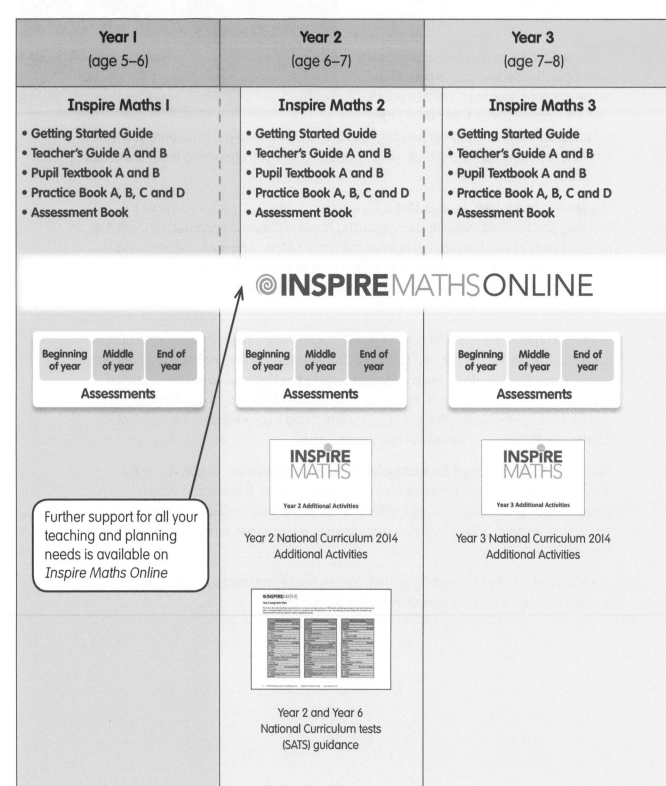

Year I (age 5–6)	Year 2 (age 6–7)	Year 3 (age 7–8)
Inspire Maths I	**Inspire Maths 2**	**Inspire Maths 3**
• Getting Started Guide • Teacher's Guide A and B • Pupil Textbook A and B • Practice Book A, B, C and D • Assessment Book	• Getting Started Guide • Teacher's Guide A and B • Pupil Textbook A and B • Practice Book A, B, C and D • Assessment Book	• Getting Started Guide • Teacher's Guide A and B • Pupil Textbook A and B • Practice Book A, B, C and D • Assessment Book

@INSPIREMATHSONLINE

Assessments: Beginning of year | Middle of year | End of year

Further support for all your teaching and planning needs is available on *Inspire Maths Online*

Year 2 National Curriculum 2014 Additional Activities

Year 3 National Curriculum 2014 Additional Activities

Year 2 and Year 6 National Curriculum tests (SATS) guidance

The Pupil Textbooks for *Inspire Maths* may cross over year borders

Year 4 (age 8–9)	Year 5 (age 9–10)	Year 6 (age 10–11)
Inspire Maths 4 • Getting Started Guide • Teacher's Guide A and B • Pupil Textbook A and B • Practice Book A and B • Assessment Book	**Inspire Maths 5** • Getting Started Guide • Teacher's Guide A and B • Pupil Textbook A and B • Practice Book A and B • Assessment Book	**Inspire Maths 6** • Getting Started Guide • Teacher's Guide A and B • Pupil Textbook A and B • Practice Book A and B • Assessment Book

Additional resources: CPD videos, Simmering Skills, transition materials, planning guides and more (on www.oxfordowl.co.uk)

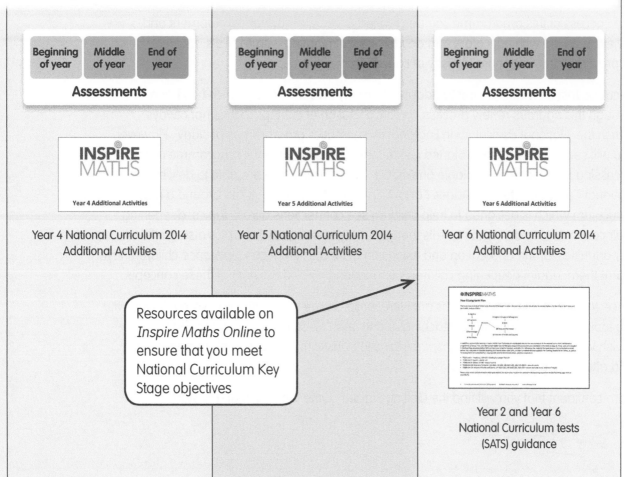

Beginning of year	Middle of year	End of year

Assessments

INSPIRE MATHS

Year 4 Additional Activities

Year 4 National Curriculum 2014 Additional Activities

Beginning of year	Middle of year	End of year

Assessments

INSPIRE MATHS

Year 5 Additional Activities

Year 5 National Curriculum 2014 Additional Activities

Beginning of year	Middle of year	End of year

Assessments

INSPIRE MATHS

Year 6 Additional Activities

Year 6 National Curriculum 2014 Additional Activities

Resources available on *Inspire Maths Online* to ensure that you meet National Curriculum Key Stage objectives

Year 2 and Year 6 National Curriculum tests (SATS) guidance

Foreword by Dr Fong Ho Kheong

Inspire Maths was introduced to the UK in 2015 and is an adaptation of the maths programme that I developed in Singapore, *My Pals are Here!*. This highly regarded mathematics programme has been used by Singapore children since 2001 and is currently being used in 80% of Singapore schools. Singapore schools have frequently ranked at the top of widely cited global studies, such as the Trends in International Mathematics and Science Study (TIMSS 2015) and the Programme for International Student Assessment (PISA 2015) (see page 9).

My Pals are Here! has found huge international success. Fifty countries have adapted mathematics materials based on the programme in print, digital and Professional Development and it has been translated into eight different languages.

I am delighted with the success *Inspire Maths* is having in raising standards of teaching and learning and promoting mastery in the UK. We have seen this impact in many different ways: for example, through a year-long independent academic study that explored the impact of the *Inspire Maths* programme; through the rise of Advocate Schools across the UK who report on how their teaching and learning has been transformed; and through the sharing of good practice by these Advocate Schools to the wider teaching community. This has translated to improvements in performance and confidence, with children working at greater depth as a result of using *Inspire Maths*.

The success of this programme can be credited to years of careful development and review, working with educators and academics, culminating with *My Pals are Here!* being approved by the Singapore Ministry of Education.

Because *Inspire Maths* is directly adapted from *My Pals are Here!*, which has been through this rigorous review process, the organisation of the topics does not always match the 'National curriculum in England: mathematics programmes of study'. However, you will see from this Getting Started Guide that by following the full programme and accessing the resources available on *Inspire Maths Online*, you are able to deliver the National Curriculum for Key Stages 1 and 2. *Inspire Maths* is structured around a mastery curriculum which is designed to help children see connections across topics, deepening their conceptual understanding. This thoughtful organisation of the topics also provides opportunities for the application and extension of fundamental concepts once children have learnt them; again, deepening children's understanding and mastery of these concepts.

Since *Inspire Maths* is the *My Pals are Here!* programme in its entirety, it will equip you with the tools to deliver high-quality teaching and to improve standards in your school. I wish you all the best in using *Inspire Maths* to transform your children's understanding and attainment in mathematics.

I am confident that you will find the Getting Started Guide the best place to start.

Dr Fong Ho Kheong

Principal author and consultant for *Inspire Maths*

PISA Results: Maths [1]
2015 (2012)

Rank	Country	Score
1 (2)	Singapore	564 (573)
2 (3)	Hong Kong (China)	548 (561)
3 (6)	Macao (China)	544 (538)
4 (4)	Taiwan	542 (560)
5 (7)	Japan	532 (536)
6 (1– as Shanghai)	Beijing-Shanghai-Jiangsu-Guangdong (China)	531 (613 – as Shanghai)
7 (5)	South Korea	524 (554)
8 (9)	Switzerland	521 (531)
9 (11)	Estonia	520 (521)
10 (13)	Canada	516 (518)
11 (10)	Netherlands	512 (523)
12 (22)	Denmark	511 (500)
13 (12)	Finland	511 (519)
14 (21)	Slovenia	510 (501)
15 (15)	Belgium	507 (515)
16 (16)	Germany	506 (514)
17 (14)	Poland	504 (518)
18 (20)	Republic of Ireland	504 (501)
19 (30)	Norway	502 (489)
20 (18)	Austria	497 (506)
21 (23)	New Zealand	495 (500)
22 (17)	Vietnam	495 (511)
23 (34)	Russia	494 (482)
24 (38)	Sweden	494 (478)
25 (19)	Australia	494 (504)
26 (25)	France	493 (495)
27 (26)	**United Kingdom**	**492 (494)**
28 (24)	Czech Republic	492 (499)
29 (31)	Portugal	492 (487)
30 (32)	Italy	490 (485)

---

1 Data taken from http://www.oecd.org/pisa/pisa-2015-results-in-focus.pdf

Proof of impact and research base in *Inspire Maths*

International tests

Inspire Maths was introduced to the UK in 2015 based on the huge success of *My Pals Are Here!* in Singapore, and internationally, where it has been translated into eight different languages and adapted in fifty countries. The evidence of hard data in the PISA and TIMSS studies supported this decision. TIMSS (Trends in International Mathematics and Science Study) is designed to help countries all over the world improve student learning in mathematics and science, whilst PISA (Programme for International Student Assessment) studies literacy in three competence fields: reading, mathematics, and science. These studies collect educational achievement data and provide information about trends in performance over time (see **Foreword by Dr Fong Ho Kheong**, pages 8–9).

Dr Fong Ho Kheong cited the 2012 PISA Survey in his Teacher's Guide Foreword to *Inspire Maths*. Singapore children continue to be at the top of world rankings for achievement in mathematics according to the 2015 PISA Survey, and 2015 TIMSS ranking tables. Crucially, the data for high and low performers shows that the systematic, consistent approach to teaching for mastery in Singapore improves outcomes for *all* children, not just the high performers. A highly supportive, highly developed and structured, research-based textbook is of central importance to the teaching and learning of mathematics, and therefore the success of children, as you will see in the following section, **High achievement in mathematics and the importance of high-quality textbooks**.

Inspire Maths impact study

A number of international research studies have shown the educational effectiveness of programmes that follow the Singapore approach to teaching mathematics but, until recently, there had been no comparable study in the UK. In 2015–2016, an independent year-long study by the Department of Education, University of Oxford, entitled *Evaluation of the Impact and Implementation of Inspire Maths in Year 1 Classrooms in England*[1] followed 576 Year 1 children for one school year. These were some of the first schools to implement both *Inspire Maths* and the 2014 English National Curriculum. By looking beyond children's attainment in mathematics, this experimental study had a broader scope than many other research studies. Changes to teacher practices and children's attitudes towards mathematics were also included in this study.

---

1 Hall J., Lindorff A. and Sammons P., *Evaluation of the Impact and Implementation of Inspire Maths in Year 1 Classrooms in England; Findings from a Mixed-Method Randomised Control Trial.* (Department of Education, University of Oxford, Oxford 2016): https://ore.exeter.ac.uk/repository/handle/10871/24265

Using data from age-appropriate versions of the Progress Test in Maths (PTM)[2] mathematics tests aligned to the National Curriculum introduced in September 2014, the study's key findings were that:

- *Inspire Maths* can help Year 1 children make significantly more progress in mathematics; large gains were observed after two terms

- *Inspire Maths* promotes Year 1 teaching practices (concrete–pictorial–abstract approach [CPA], variation theory, deep conceptual understanding, teaching for mastery) that are well known to be more effective for children's progress in the long term.

Teachers noted a number of key benefits and challenges to themselves, children and schools when implementing *Inspire Maths*. These were quite consistent regardless of whether a teacher began implementing *Inspire Maths* in September or in January.

- Benefits to classroom practice were noted immediately following initial professional development training workshops. Secondary benefits were then observed over the course of the year.

In addition:

- Teachers were positive about the *Inspire Maths* materials and approach as well as the support provided by Oxford University Press.[3]

- Teachers reported that the programme boosted children's motivation and engagement, and that *Inspire Maths* was used creatively and flexibly.

James Hall, lead-author, and now Lecturer at the University of Exeter, said:

Overall we found positive evidence that *Inspire Maths* benefited children's mathematics achievement and supported teachers' professional development. This boost to progress was surprising because children had only been in a classroom setting for a short period and because it often takes time to embed new teaching approaches.[4]

2 PTM, GL Assessment, 2015, http://www.gl-assessment.co.uk/products/progress-test-maths

3 Hall J., Lindorff A. and Sammons P., *Evaluation of the Impact and Implementation of Inspire Maths in Year 1 Classrooms in England; Findings from a Mixed-Method Randomised Control Trial.* (Department of Education, University of Oxford, Oxford 2016): https://ore.exeter.ac.uk/repository/handle/10871/24265

4 University of Exeter, 'Research reveals that "Singapore" approach to teaching maths can work in UK classrooms', 2016: http://www.exeter.ac.uk/news/featurednews/title_550537_en.html

Inspire Maths Advocate Schools

Among the schools using *Inspire Maths* in the UK, reports of rising maths attainment, backed by SATs results, are continuously fed back to Oxford University Press. The *Inspire Maths* Evaluation by Oxford University included comments that teachers wanted to see examples of successful lessons. To meet this need, schools demonstrating high-quality *Inspire Maths* teaching are invited to become Advocate Schools. The purpose is to offer head teachers and maths leaders who are considering using *Inspire Maths* for their own schools an opportunity to see lessons in action and question teaching staff who use *Inspire Maths*. This approach builds a strong professional learning community amongst schools using *Inspire Maths*, for them to support each other and share best practice – a key aim of all *Inspire Maths* professional development.

In order to become an Advocate School, the school (or at least two members of the senior leadership team) will have had five days of *Inspire Maths* professional development. The school will have implemented *Inspire Maths* for at least one year and demonstrate engaging, high-quality, exemplary teaching in a learning environment where children are confident learners and are being encouraged to engage in mathematical conversations and reflect on their learning. The Advocate School receives ongoing support through regular contact and professional development, which is tailored to that school and its needs.

Quantitative and qualitative data continues to provide evidence of the exceptional impact of *Inspire Maths*. Independent primary mathematics education consultants work with schools and provide ongoing professional development. This affords a unique insight into what is working well in schools and where further support is needed.

These consultants have identified recurring themes of children developing a strong understanding of number, a deep and lasting procedural and conceptual mathematical understanding and an increase in confidence. In addition to raising attainment, *Inspire Maths* demonstrably increases teachers' enjoyment and confidence in teaching, whilst concurrently increasing children's enthusiasm for mathematics lessons.

Over the next few pages you will read case studies from schools using *Inspire Maths* about the positive impact it has had in the classroom, for both children and teachers.

Wentworth Primary School[5]

School Profile[6]

Head Teacher: Paul Langridge

Town: Dartford

Local Authority: Kent

Children on roll: 535

% of pupils eligible for free school meals at any time during the past 6 years: 13·1%

% of pupils whose first language is not English: 11%

Ofsted: Good, February 2013

Wentworth Primary School was 'average' in the 2017 KS2 SATs in Mathematics at −0·4 and +0·4 in the 2016 KS2 SATs.

Wentworth Primary School's best practice was showcased in the 2017 Parliamentary Review. Paul Langridge took over the position as head teacher in September 2015, aware that a major overhaul had to be undertaken to combat a challenging set of circumstances, and he describes the key changes he has made, one of them in mathematics.

"A review of mathematics in December 2015 identified a number of children who had left Key Stage 1 with gaps in their knowledge and understanding. They had learnt tricks and 'quick fixes' instead of developing sound conceptual understanding. Our planning process was immediately overhauled to ensure that learning was leading the planning rather than vice versa. Following an analysis of several mathematics schemes and visiting pilot schools, I decided to introduce *Inspire Maths* to Years 1 and 2. *Inspire Maths* is very much based on the Singapore Mathematics curriculum and ensures that children develop a strong understanding of number, giving them secure knowledge in order to understand and explain how and why they know. This was further supported by training in September 2016, which was described as 'inspirational' by our staff. Children throughout the school now follow a mathematical process based on the CPA approach. Problem solving has become much more successful, with children now applying the Singapore Bar Method to their reasoning. It is immensely satisfying to watch children experience a 'lightbulb' moment where they smile and recognise that they 'get it!' More importantly, they understand HOW and WHY they 'got it'. *Inspire Maths* will move into Year 3 and then be assimilated through the school.

At Wentworth, learning is based on collective development, where the strengths of individuals are recognised and support is provided to maximise the potential of all."

---

5 Adapted from 'Primary Education South of England 2017', The Parliamentary Review (Westminster Publications, London): http://theparliamentaryreview.co.uk/editions/primary-education/primary-south

6 Department of Education, 'Wentworth Primary School', 2016–2017: https://www.compare-school-performance.service.gov.uk/school/137836?tab=absence-and-pupil-population

Moreland Primary School

School Profile[7]

Head of School: Chris Quinton

Mathematics Leader: Nim Kimyani

Town: London

Local Authority: Islington

Children on roll: 275

% of pupils eligible for free school meals at any time during the past 6 years: 60%

% of pupils whose first language is not English: 68·6%

Ofsted: Good, March 2016

Moreland Primary School was 'well above average' in the 2017 KS2 SATs in Mathematics at +3·5 and at +6·2 in the 2016 KS2 SATs.

Moreland Primary School in Islington, London has been nationally recognised for its excellence by Minister of State, Department of Education, Nick Gibb MP

What impact have the *Inspire Maths* Textbooks and Practice books had on your children's engagement, learning and understanding?

The children love the CPA approach and enjoy how the textbooks and practice books allow them to become more independent learners. They feel much more in control of their learning journey – the books have allowed us to move away from whole-class teaching and towards an emphasis on exploration and guided practice. The children have responded incredibly well to this systemic set-up, and it has truly transformed their engagement with mathematics. They particularly like the fact that they have more time to practise new concepts and have become much more aware of patterns and connections between concepts, and of how their knowledge is building over time.

How supportive do teachers at your school find the *Inspire Maths* teaching materials?

Teachers have found that *Inspire Maths* really supports and scaffolds their subject knowledge, and there is no longer pressure to race through topics. Instead, the emphasis is much more on teaching concepts to mastery and building really firm foundations. Rather than spending time thinking about *what* to teach they can concentrate their time and efforts on *how* to teach. Additionally, time is no longer wasted searching for resources as *Inspire Maths* provides all the materials that teachers need. Teachers are particularly impressed with the quality and depth of the questioning and the level of challenge available for our more able children. They have found that the children have

---

7 Department of Education, 'Moreland Primary School', 2016–2017: https://www.compare-school-performance.service.gov.uk/school/100415?tab=absence-and-pupil-population

become much more independent, which gives them more time to concentrate on helping those children who might not grasp a concept the first time.

Would you recommend *Inspire Maths* to other schools and, if yes, is there one reason above all others that you would give?

Inspire Maths has transformed the teaching and learning of mathematics in our school to such an extent that it is hard to choose just one reason above all others – but if pushed it would be the engagement that the children have with the subject now. It has made our children much more resilient and independent learners, with a real love and curiosity about mathematics; all supported by a much better understanding of the fundamentals.

The successful work to introduce and rapidly embed *Inspire Maths* has made significant improvements in teaching and progress in mathematics.

Ofsted Report, April 2016

St Paul's C of E Primary School

School Profile[8]

Assistant Head Teacher: Jackie Graham

Town: Sunderland

Local Authority: Sunderland

Children on roll: 234

% of pupils eligible for free school meals at any time during the past 6 years: 17·6%

% of pupils whose first language is not English: 0·6%

Ofsted: Good, October 2013

St Paul's Church of England Primary school was 'well above average' in the 2017 KS2 SATs in Mathematics at +4·8, and at +7·9 in the 2016 KS2 SATs.

What impact/benefit has *Inspire Maths* had on teaching, learning and understanding?

The CPA approach has improved our teachers' understanding of how children learn mathematics and how children can access mathematics as a whole, but in different ways. It has proved invaluable in supporting the middle and low attainers, who have flourished and, in some cases, outshone those who were previously deemed to be more able. I can't wait to see the effects as our '*Inspire Maths* children' progress through the school.

How do you use *Inspire Maths* to meet the expectations of the National Curriculum?

At the moment, we use *Inspire Maths* in Years 1 and 2 and we use the curriculum mapping document to ensure full coverage of the NC objectives. Any which are not included are then taught discretely or in a cross-curricular approach.

On a scale of 1 to 5, how likely would you be to recommend *Inspire Maths* to other schools and what would you say to other schools who are considering purchasing *Inspire Maths*?

5 – highly likely. *Inspire Maths* has given our teachers the confidence and scaffolding to fully embrace a mastery approach and the standards can be seen as soon as I open the books and speak to the children. Our children are adept at explaining their thinking and their reasoning skills are developing rapidly. The implementation and logistics of *Inspire Maths* have not been without their teething problems, but they are minor when compared to the benefits we have gained as a school.

8 Department of Education, 'St Paul's CofE Primary School', 2016–2017: https://www.compare-school-performance.service.gov.uk/school/108836?tab=absence-and-pupil-population

St Joseph's Roman Catholic Primary School

School Profile[9]

Head Teacher: Anne O'Brien

Town: Darwen

Local Authority: Blackburn with Darwen

Children on roll: 144

% of pupils eligible for free school meals at any time during the past 6 years: 20·2%

% of pupils whose first language is not English: 5%

Ofsted: Good, October 2015

St Joseph's Roman Catholic Primary School was 'average' in the 2017 KS2 SATs in Mathematics at -0·8, and at +0·7 in the 2016 KS2 SATs. However, in 2016 children had made significant progress from their KS1 score.

What impact have the *Inspire Maths* Textbooks and Practice Books had on your children's engagement, learning and understanding?

The children love the approach. The learning moves on in small but challenging steps, so that in no time the children have moved from a quite basic level of understanding to something quite challenging. Conceptually, we've never seen anything as complete. The children's deeper understanding is constantly reinforced.

What has been the trend of improvement since using *Inspire Maths*?

What we can see immediately is that the children are gaining a much more secure understanding of the mathematics concepts being taught. We can see some of the weaknesses in our previous (and very well intentioned) methods.

Which activities have been particularly successful with your children, and why?

All of them, really! However, conservation of number in Year 1 has been particularly enhanced as children explore everything there is to know about 12, for example. We are also moving very much towards a growth mind-set approach. This has had a very positive impact on children who were traditionally lower achievers as they are now much more included in whole-class lessons. We love it.

9 Department of Education, 'St Joseph's Roman Catholic Primary School, Darwen', 2016–2017: https://www.compare-school-performance.service.gov.uk/school/119667?tab=absence-and-pupil-population

High achievement in mathematics and the importance of high-quality textbooks

The importance of high-quality textbooks

When we look at recent results from the Trends in International Mathematics and Science Study (TIMSS) and the Programme for International Student Assessment (PISA) studies, high-performing jurisdictions in the Far East, such as Singapore, consistently top the international league tables for child-performance in mathematics. Mathematics teaching in these countries is characterised by a diligent and systematic approach to the curriculum and teaching, which enables all children to succeed. There are various features of 'teaching for mastery', including the use of high-quality, successful textbooks. These research-based, proven textbooks are carefully structured and highly supportive for both teachers and children.

PISA Results: Maths[1] 2015 (2012)		
Rank	**Country**	**Score**
1 (2)	Singapore	564 (573)
2 (3)	Hong Kong (China)	548 (561)
3 (6)	Macao (China)	544 (538)
4 (4)	Taiwan	542 (560)
5 (7)	Japan	532 (536)
6 (1– as Shanghai)	Beijing-Shanghai-Jiangsu-Guangdong (China)	531 (613 – as Shanghai)
7 (5)	South Korea	524 (554)
8 (9)	Switzerland	521 (531)
9 (11)	Estonia	520 (521)
10 (13)	Canada	516 (518)
11 (10)	Netherlands	512 (523)
12 (22)	Denmark	511 (500)
13 (12)	Finland	511 (519)
14 (21)	Slovenia	510 (501)
15 (15)	Belgium	507 (515)
16 (16)	Germany	506 (514)
17 (14)	Poland	504 (518)
18 (20)	Republic of Ireland	504 (501)
19 (30)	Norway	502 (489)
20 (18)	Austria	497 (506)
21 (23)	New Zealand	495 (500)
22 (17)	Vietnam	495 (511)
23 (34)	Russia	494 (482)
24 (38)	Sweden	494 (478)
25 (19)	Australia	494 (504)
26 (25)	France	493 (495)
27 (26)	**United Kingdom**	**492 (494)**
28 (24)	Czech Republic	492 (499)
29 (31)	Portugal	492 (487)
30 (32)	Italy	490 (485)

1 Data taken from http://www.oecd.org/pisa/pisa-2015-results-in-focus.pdf

Tim Oates CBE, Group Director of Assessment Research and Development, Cambridge Assessment, was commissioned in 2010 to lead the UK government's review of the 'National curriculum in England: mathematics programmes of study'. The study investigated the use of high-quality textbooks in key nations, how they support teachers and children, and the impact on the teaching and learning of mathematics. His resulting policy paper in 2014 concluded that high-quality textbooks are a vital part of successful implementation of a national curriculum.

He found that:

"high-quality textbooks are not antithetical to high-quality pedagogy – they are supportive of sensitive and effective approaches to high attainment, high equity and high enjoyment of learning".[2]

The National Centre for Excellence in the Teaching of Mathematics (NCETM) guidance on the principles of a well-designed and well-researched mathematics textbook, points out that:

"A high-quality mathematics textbook is an educational resource that can be used by pupils both in lessons and independently, and that also provides both subject knowledge and pedagogy support to teachers of mathematics. It is a comprehensive learning tool, providing support for the development of both procedural fluency and conceptual understanding in mathematics: a textbook consisting only of worked examples and simple repetitive exercises is unlikely to develop these. It is essential that the principles under-pinning teaching with variation are reflected in the choice of examples and the structure of the exercises. Pupils must be provided with frequent opportunities for intelligent practice."[3]

Vanessa Pittard, independent education consultant and former Department for Education (DfE) Assistant Director, goes further, saying that:

"For primary teachers, who in the UK and Singapore are not [mathematics] subject specialists, well-designed textbooks do more: they help deepen subject knowledge and develop professional understanding of effective teaching methods. High-quality mathematics textbook series found in Singapore and other leading jurisdictions include pupil textbooks, teacher guides and practice books. Teacher guides serve as essential manuals for teachers: they distil key concepts, clarify objectives and set out logical teaching sequences drawing on the content of the vital pupil textbook."[4]

In Singapore, currently the leading jurisdiction internationally for mathematics child-performance, the high quality of textbooks is upheld through a rigorous textbook review process. These textbooks are research based and the content is continually tested, reviewed and refined through classroom practice. The rigorous review process by a panel of professionals including educators and academics from the universities culminates in the materials being approved by the Ministry of Education. This means that *My Pals are Here!* (Marshall Cavendish), Singapore's leading mathematics textbook programme, has been continually refined for over seventeen years.

---

2 Oates, T (2014) Why Textbooks Count, Cambridge Assessment. http://www.cambridgeassessment.org.uk/news/new-research-shows-why-textbooks-count-tim-oates/
3 https://www.ncetm.org.uk/files/21383193/NCETM+Textbook+Guidance.pdf
4 https://educationblog.oup.com/primary/mastery-myths-textbooks-constrain-creative-teaching

Inspire Maths textbooks

Inspire Maths is the UK edition of *My Pals Are Here!*. It provides a logical, detailed curriculum progression and lesson content, with rigorous supporting materials for non-specialist primary school teachers of mathematics. This enables consistency both within schools and between schools, and for every teacher to teach to a consistently high standard and to meet the exacting requirements of the National Curriculum.

The development of the curriculum within *Inspire Maths* focuses on slow, secure building of mathematical knowledge, with whole-class interactive teaching, high expectations for all, plenty of guided and independent practice and a focus on deep conceptual understanding.

The concrete–pictorial–abstract (CPA) approach is inherent throughout the textbooks with teaching for both understanding and fluency. New concepts are introduced concretely with rigorous support for children to move towards abstract and procedural mathematics with understanding. There is a consistent use of models and images to support the development of new concepts, which means a secure, long-term, and deep conceptual understanding of mathematics.

Inspire Maths provides detailed support for teachers on lesson sequence, what to look and listen for, subject knowledge, lesson planning, suggested higher-order questions to support and challenge reasoning, and questions to support assessment. Drawing on variation theory, which emphasises the importance of children experiencing the same mathematical concept in carefully varied ways, *Inspire Maths* builds on understanding, in carefully designed steps, in order for children to develop deep, conceptual understanding as they progress towards mastery. The textbooks are equally supportive for teachers and children.

Inspire Maths has had a huge impact on our whole-school approach to mathematics. We feel that we are now addressing the three main National Curriculum aims through a more structured and connected programme. Through the professional development that we have received and the detailed Teacher Guides, our teachers have developed a deeper understanding of how children become successful mathematicians. By implementing *Inspire Maths* across our school it has brought a new found vibrancy towards the teaching and learning of mathematics.

St Thomas CE Primary School, Blackburn

Inspire Maths Professional Development

Teachers are also supported through *Inspire Maths* Continuing Professional Development to develop a pedagogical understanding of the Singapore approach to teaching and learning mathematics, to understand how to use the textbooks and to build capacity to successfully implement *Inspire Maths*, ensuring sustained learning and achievement.

In March 2017, the report of the Independent Teacher Workload Review Group found that:

> *"Teachers spend an undue amount of time planning and resourcing lessons, and there are clear measures that should be taken by Government, Ofsted, schools, and teachers to lessen this burden."* [5]

Inspire Maths professional development consultants visit schools and work with teachers who are teaching for mastery. Teachers using *Inspire Maths* say that they have been able to change the way they plan, so that they don't have to spend time deciding *what* to teach and can invest more of their time in designing their lessons and considering *how* they teach. They find the *Inspire Maths* Teachers Guides highly supportive because they detail what needs to be taught and how, ensuring excellent progression within the subject.

Three Legged Cross First and Nursery School, Dorset, who teach mathematics with *Inspire Maths*, say that their results improved because of:

> Teacher confidence, greater continuity of teaching and improved consistency, deeper knowledge of concepts taught for children, clearer progression.

As a teacher, you know that the textbooks do not do the teaching. You are responsible for the teaching and learning and it's important that you understand the approach taken within the textbooks. *Inspire Maths* is highly supportive for both specialist and non-specialist mathematics teachers, providing detailed guidance on what to teach and how to teach through a progression in small steps, which is fundamental to teaching for mastery.

> *"… having access to an elegant, coherent and comprehensive resource makes it easier. Teachers are liberated to focus on designing and delivering the engaging, interactive lessons which are characteristic of mastery teaching.*
>
> *Not only this, children have a resource to return to and consult, and teachers have access to a well-designed set of ready-made exercises for practice and assessment, lightening the load further and reinforcing what's taught."* [6]

> Vanessa Pittard

---

5 Eliminating unnecessary workload around planning and teaching resources: https://www.atl.org.uk/policy-and-campaigns/policy-posts/tackling-workload-together
6 https://educationblog.oup.com/primary/mastery-myths-textbooks-constrain-creative-teaching

Children learning mathematics with *Inspire Maths* often say how much they love it. One of the things they say they like is that if they forget what to do or how to do it, they can use the textbooks to remind themselves what has gone before and what they are working towards.

The research underpinning the mathematical content and its organisation minimises the risk of children getting confused, misunderstanding concepts or experiencing cognitive overload. In addition, the organisation of the topics in *Inspire Maths* helps children see connections across the subject, which is helpful in deepening their conceptual understanding.

The benefits of using high-quality textbooks

High-quality textbooks such as *Inspire Maths* have a profound impact on the teaching and learning of mathematics. They set out a well-proven, detailed and connected curriculum, which provides schools with cohesion across academic years and support in school curriculum planning. They provide teachers with a highly supportive teaching guide, and can scaffold your understanding of effective maths pedagogy, thus ensuring that lessons are consistently of a high standard. Teachers can be further supported through professional development for the textbook programme and raising standards in the teaching and learning of mathematics. Using a high-quality textbook reduces the time teachers spend finding resources and planning their lessons, so that teachers can dedicate their time to designing lessons. Finally, the textbook programme provides coherent resources for pedagogy, conceptual understanding, practice, assessment and further challenge, so it should be used comprehensively for maximum benefit for teachers and children. High-quality textbooks support effective teaching, enhance teacher subject knowledge, build children's confidence and deepen their conceptual understanding, enabling them to become confident mathematicians, embarking on a lifelong love of mathematics.

As you read through this Getting Started Guide, you will understand the benefits of using *Inspire Maths*, with practical examples of how the programme supports the teaching and learning in your classroom.

Pace, progression and fidelity

Inspire Maths – the UK edition of the authentic Singapore programme

Inspire Maths is the UK edition of the highly-regarded Singapore textbook programme *My Pals are Here!*, which has been used in Singaporean schools since 2001. Therefore, *Inspire Maths* follows the Singapore mathematics curriculum which builds knowledge systematically in small cumulative steps. In adapting *Inspire Maths* for the UK, the only content changes made were to contexts and references such as currency and place names to make them more familiar to our children. The essential content of *My Pals are Here!* was purposely left intact, since it had been regularly reviewed, tested extensively in practice, revised and approved by the Ministry of Education in Singapore. The *My Pals are Here!* programme was written to support non-specialist maths teachers and primary maths teachers in raising the attainment of average children. The content, spiral approach and progression, based on extensive research, such as the Cockcroft Report (published in 1982)[1], enabled Singaporean children to climb to the top of international independent studies of maths attainment, such as PISA (Programme for International Student Assessment), and TIMSS (Trends in International Mathematics and Science Study) since 1995, where they have remained since. The carefully designed curriculum is one of the factors which contribute to Singapore's success.

The Singapore curriculum is specially designed to ensure that all children succeed in learning maths by developing a deep understanding of the concepts. It is characterised by purposeful organisation of topics, and covering concepts for deep understanding.

Purposeful organisation of topics in *Inspire Maths*

The sequencing of the topics in *Inspire Maths* takes into consideration children's cognitive development to facilitate the maximum mastery of key concepts. For example, measurement and arithmetic topics reflect Piaget's work on cognitive development, specifically in the concrete operational stage. Piaget's ideas inform the sequencing of concrete activities and *Inspire Maths* adopts Bruner's concrete–pictorial–abstract (CPA) approach when concepts are introduced. This approach supports the transition from manipulation of concrete objects to mental representations, the development of mathematical language and the internalisation of strategies required to operate mathematically. See **How to teach with *Inspire Maths*** on pages 38–57 for further details on the CPA approach.

Geometry topics are organised according to the Van Hiele levels of geometry understanding. Pierre Van Hiele and Dina Van Hiele-Geldof[2] developed a theoretical model involving five levels of thought development in geometry. This model involves a systematic approach to children's development of geometrical ideas. To be on a particular level a child has to consistently exhibit behaviours indicative of that level. The levels give

---

1 Cockcroft, W. H., The Cockcroft Report: Mathematics Counts (Her Majesty's Stationery Office, London, 1982): http://www. educationengland.org.uk/documents/cockcroft/cockcroft1982.html [accessed 8 January 2018]

2 van Hiele, P. M., A child's thought and geometry. In D. Fuys, D. Geddes, & R. Tischler (Eds.), *English translation of selected writings of Dina van Hiele-Geldof and P. M. van Hiele* (Brooklyn: Brooklyn College, 1984) [Original document in French: La pensee de l'enfant et la geometrie, Bulletin de l'Association des Professeurs de Mathematiques de l'Enseignment Public. 1959]

a clear picture of the processes and stages children go through to reach a secure and abstract level of geometric understanding, from level I (recognising and visualising shapes) to level 5 (formal geometrical reasoning).

The world-class research underpinning the sequencing of the programme minimises the risk of any cognitive overload. Furthermore, the organisation of the topics in *Inspire Maths* helps children to make connections across topics, which is helpful in deepening their conceptual understanding.

Hiebert and Lefevre (1986)[3] talk about the importance of these connections,

> *"Conceptual knowledge is characterised most clearly as knowledge that is rich in relationships. It can be thought of as a connected web of knowledge, a network in which the linking relationships are as important as the discrete pieces of information. Relationships pervade the individual facts and propositions so that all pieces of information are linked to some network."*

This connected web of knowledge is integral to *Inspire Maths*. An example of this is the way children learn how to tell the time in *Inspire Maths*. In *Inspire Maths* I, they learn to tell the time to the hour and half hour and compare and sequence intervals of time. In *Inspire Maths* 2, children start by telling and writing the time to five minutes, including quarter past and quarter to the hour and drawing hands on an analogue clock to show times given. Children use their knowledge and understanding of multiplying by five to make a connection between the five times table and telling the time. Doing so deepens children's conceptual understanding, which is an essential part of maths mastery.

The organisation of topics in *Inspire Maths* also provides opportunities for the application and extension of fundamental concepts, once children have learnt them, to help deepen their understanding and mastery. For example, in *Inspire Maths* I, children become secure in comparing and ordering numbers up to 100 and the place value of digits in a 2-digit number. In *Inspire Maths* 2, children build on their knowledge of the place value of tens and ones to learn about the place value of hundreds in 3-digit numbers. They then apply their knowledge to compare and order 3-digit numbers up to 1000. Children's understanding of place value is developed throughout *Inspire Maths*, culminating in *Inspire Maths* 5 when children will be working with numbers up to 10 million, rounding to the nearest hundred and nearest thousand, multiplying and dividing by 10, 100 and 1000, and eventually working with decimals up to three decimal places.

In *Inspire Maths* I and 2, children learn addition, subtraction, multiplication and division. Children then apply their understanding of numbers and the four operations to practical problems, which is a Key Stage 2 topic but is introduced earlier to align with Skemp's theory on relational learning.[4] Children should not learn skills and concepts in isolation; instead, they should see the relationships among these concepts to bridge any cognitive gap and make learning more meaningful. It is therefore important that children are given ample opportunities to apply their skills operationally, and put their knowledge into practice, thereby enabling them to master the concepts and skills in operations.

---

3 Hiebert, J., and Lefevre, P. Conceptual and procedural knowledge in mathematics: An introductory analysis. In J. Hiebert (ed.), *Conceptual and Procedural Knowledge: The Case of Mathematics*. (Hillsdale, NJ: Lawrence Erlbaum Associates, 1986), pp.3–4.

4 Skemp, Richard R. Relational Understanding and Instrumental Understanding (Warwick: Department of Education, University of Warwick, 1976): https://www.atm.org.uk/write/MediaUploads/Resources/Richard_Skemp.pdf

In-depth development of individual concepts in *Inspire Maths*

In *Inspire Maths*, concepts in each topic are carefully developed using Piaget's Assimilation and Accommodation Approach[5]. This ensures that sufficient time is given for children to master each concept before they move on to the next.

Piagetian conceptual development takes place over four stages:

- **Learn**: Direct teaching to develop knowledge and deep understanding.

- **Guided practice**: Informal assessment of children's understanding.

- **Activity**: Help for children to accommodate the concepts and skills learnt.

- **Practice**: Further enhancement to the accommodation of concepts and skills.

The structure of the *Inspire Maths* programme mirrors these stages through the teaching sequence 'Let's Learn', 'Guided Practice', 'Activity' and 'Independent Practice'. With this structure, children have ample opportunities to practise concepts in *Inspire Maths*, and the scaffolded approach of practice gradually releases the responsibility of learning to the children.

During 'Guided Practice', children practise concepts with teacher's guidance and you have the opportunity to identify those who need immediate intervention, consolidation, further practice or challenge to go deeper. This contributes to making learning accessible to all, and by the time children reach the second stage of practice, which is done independently, they will be able to answer the questions confidently. This cycle of conceptual development repeats each time a new concept is introduced so mastery is achieved in a structured and coherent manner, without the risk of any child falling behind.

A spiral, cumulative approach

The spiral, cumulative approach relies on building mathematical content progressively over time, so it is strongly recommended you teach the content in *Inspire Maths* in the order it is presented. There are some 'National curriculum in England: mathematics programmes of study' objectives not covered by the Pupil Textbooks. You will find 'Additional Activities' on *Inspire Maths Online* (www.oxfordowl.co.uk) to support you to meet these (see **How *Inspire Maths* relates to the National Curriculum** for further guidance). There are also some topics introduced earlier in *Inspire Maths* than in the National Curriculum. You can be confident that all relevant objectives will be covered by the end of each Key Stage when you use the Pupil Textbooks and the additional activities on *Inspire Maths Online*.

As *Inspire Maths* follows the Singapore maths curriculum progression, it is structured by stage rather than by age so it is not necessary to cover all the content in, for example, *Inspire Maths* 2 in Year 2. Children can continue working on *Inspire Maths* 2 in Year 3. At the start of each academic year, the appropriate starting point should be considered after liaising with the previous class teacher and the needs of the class. Please refer to the chart on pages 6–7 for a guide to teaching and using the *Inspire Maths* Pupil Textbooks across the academic years.

---

5 Hall J., Lindorff A. and Sammons P., *Evaluation of the Impact and Implementation of Inspire Maths in Year 1 Classrooms in England: Findings from a Mixed-Method Randomised Control Trial* (Department of Education, University of Oxford, Oxford 2016): https://ore.exeter.ac.uk/repository/handle/10871/24265

The importance of appropriate pace

The medium-term plans in the Teacher's Guides give you an indication of how many weeks you might spend covering a particular section in a unit, together with the learning objectives, an outline of the thinking skills and textbook resources you will need when teaching the section. However it is important to remember that this is only guidance; for example, you do not need to cover all of *Inspire Maths* I in Year I. Some teachers ask about the amount of time they should spend on a particular topic. The weeks allocated in the long-term planning are only a guide. Depending on how quickly a particular cohort gains a secure grasp of the content, you may spend more or less time on particular units from one year to the next. The important thing is not to rush children through the content. You may find it helpful to annotate your Teacher's Guide, making a careful note of how long it took your children to demonstrate a deep conceptual understanding.

If you find that your children are still working through, for example, *Inspire Maths* Pupil Textbook IB at the end of Year I, don't worry that you are going too slowly. Slower pace at early stages means that all children are likely to be cognitively ready as well as mathematically prepared, and therefore will be both less likely to fall behind and far more likely to progress well at later stages. The National Curriculum introduction specifies,

> *"Schools are … only required to teach the relevant programme of study by the end of the key stage. Within each key stage, schools therefore have the flexibility to introduce content earlier or later than set out in the programme of study. In addition, schools can introduce key stage content during an earlier key stage, if appropriate."[6]*

The most important thing is not to move on too quickly, because this leads to gaps in knowledge and misconceptions which, if ignored, will manifest themselves at Key Stage 4 when children take GCSEs. Going slowly ensures children have depth of understanding, rather than superficial understanding which is often unreliable. Take your time progressing through the material and allow children the time they need to develop their deep conceptual understanding.

Inspire Maths supports the National Curriculum expectation that "the majority of pupils will move through the programmes of study at broadly the same pace. However, decisions about when to progress should always be based on the security of pupils' understanding and their readiness to progress to the next stage."[7] Whilst the *Inspire Maths* medium-term plans give a suggestion of the time needed to develop a concept, it is important that you apply your professional judgement when considering whether the required understanding is in place before progressing to the next unit of work.

Fidelity to the National Curriculum

There is plenty of support and guidance on *Inspire Maths Online* to help you ensure that you have met the requirements of the National Curriculum for the relevant Key Stage, for example, there are detailed correlation charts to help you understand where key National Curriculum concepts are taught and practised in *Inspire Maths*.

---

6 Department for Education (2013), The national curriculum in England: Key stages I and 2 framework document, page I00: https://www.gov.uk/government/uploads/system/uploads/attachment_data/file/425601/PRIMARY_national_curriculum.pdf

7 Department for Education (2013), The national curriculum in England: Key stages I and 2 framework document, page 99: https://www.gov.uk/government/uploads/system/uploads/attachment_data/file/425601/PRIMARY_national_curriculum.pdf

If you are teaching Year 2 or Year 6, you will find useful charts on page 72 of the *Inspire Maths* Getting Started Guides 2 and 6 that detail the necessary content to cover for the relevant Key Stages. There are also flow charts in the 'SATs Guidance Documentation' on *Inspire Maths Online*, which suggest routes through the content to ensure that children have covered everything required for their SATs. For example, when teaching *Inspire Maths* 2, as an exception, you may need to visit the units in a different order to cover Unit II on money by the time it comes to the SATs. Refer to the guidance documents for further support. In both *Inspire Maths* 2 and *Inspire Maths* 6, you will find that there is some content that goes beyond National Curriculum expectations. Your focus should be on Key Stage I content and its consolidation for Year 2, and Key Stage 2 content and its consolidation for Year 6. If you are confident that the necessary Key Stage material has been consolidated and children are secure with deep conceptual understanding, then this material could be introduced to your children, or introduced after Key Stage I and Key Stage 2 National Curriculum tests in preparation for transition.

Some schools using *Inspire Maths* have reported that classes who spend plenty of time investigating and working with, for example, number, might appear to be progressing through the topics quite slowly, particularly in Year I when children are laying down really firm foundations. However, as a result, they can then move more quickly through later content in Key Stage 2 as their deep conceptual understanding forms a strong and reliable foundation for later progress.

Some schools may be using and implementing *Inspire Maths* in this way:

Year I	Year 2	Year 3	Year 4	Year 5	Year 6
IMI	*IM2*	*IM3*	*IM4*	*IM5*	*IM6*

Some schools may be using and implementing *Inspire Maths* like this:

Year I	Year 2	Year 3	Year 4	Year 5	Year 6
IMI	*IM2*	*IM3*	*IM4*	*IM5*	*IM6*

You will need to decide what works for you and your children but you may well use *Inspire Maths* the second way, particularly whilst you are becoming familiar with the content. It is important to remember that schools are only required to teach the relevant programme of study by the end of that Key Stage.

Inspire Maths is a proven, high-quality maths programme based on years of research and refinement and provides a secure foundation for children to become confident learners, proficient problem solvers and capable mathematicians. Our children will have an appreciation for and an enjoyment of mathematics. What better foundations and life skills can we give them?

Over the next few pages, you will find examples of how a concept is gradually and systematically developed in *Inspire Maths*. These examples show the careful progression with exemplification across all the interconnected components and give an indication of the path within each level and across *Inspire Maths*.

Pace and progression in *Inspire Maths* I: Place value

Previous learning

Before 2-digit numbers and place value are introduced, the small, logical steps building up to Unit 7 provide children with a deep, conceptual understanding of numbers to 10, including adding and subtracting up to 10. This firm foundation is required for teaching the complex concept of place value. The medium-term planning guidance suggests you spend a minimum of eight weeks teaching numbers 0–10. Throughout all the teaching, these concepts are explored with concrete apparatus, and learning is in small steps, to ensure understanding.

New learning

Unit 7 explores numbers to 20, skilfully introducing the concept of place value. The previous teaching sequence for numbers 0–10 is now repeated for numbers up to 20. The invariant nature of the teaching sequence helps children focus on the variation in the patterns in the mathematics itself. Connections are made to earlier learning with the same small, logical steps:

- Counting up to 20 in ones, then by making 10 first and counting on from 10 up to 20. This mirrors the introduction of adding up to 10 in Unit 2, where items were grouped, and additional items were added by 'counting on'. The skill and concept is the same as for numbers up to 10, only now applied to an increased amount **1**

- Adding two sets of items, using number bonds, is applied to numbers up to 20.

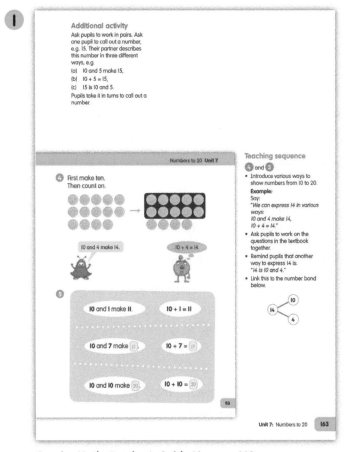

Inspire Maths **Teacher's Guide IA, page 163**

A place-value chart is only now introduced as a perceptual variation in how the numbers up to 20 can be represented as tens and ones by:

- Children using a variety of concrete materials on a place-value chart

- Children recording their use of concrete materials by drawing the representations

- Children recording their use of concrete materials by writing the digits

- Children interpreting pictures of amounts by writing the digits on a place-value chart ❶

- Children interpreting the digits on a place-value chart by drawing the concrete materials.

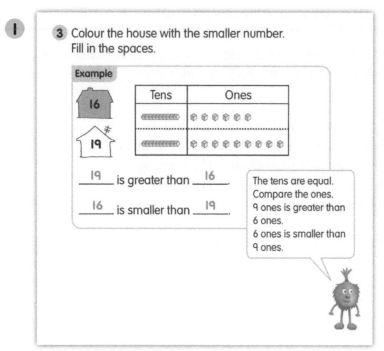

Inspire Maths **Practice Book 1B, page 63**

Moving between the concrete, pictorial and abstract representations of these numbers helps children identify 'what is the same, what is different?' about them, which draws their focus to the essential aspects of place value. This careful scaffolding of learning develops a deep and secure understanding of place value.

The teaching sequence continues, and throughout these activities, a place-value chart is consistently included in the variation of representations used, which include:

- Reading and writing numbers 11 up to 20 in numerals and words

- Understanding the 'equals' symbol where the total amount is shown first in a calculation, for example '14 = 1 ten and 4 ones', ensuring that children do not see the equals symbol as only meaning the answer to a calculation

- Partitioning numbers 10 to 20

- Comparing and ordering numbers, using the terms greater than, more than, greatest, and smaller than, fewer than and smallest

- Arranging numbers in ascending and descending order.

The medium-term planning guidance suggests you spend a minimum of two weeks on Unit 7. This will depend on how secure children are with mathematical ideas and key concepts building up to this unit. We advise that if your class take longer to understand the concepts, you do not rush through any of these units. Secure understanding of key concepts in Unit 7, Numbers to 20, is vital for the work covered in the next unit, Addition and Subtraction within 20. The 'make 10' and 'regrouping into tens and ones' strategies are used along with analysing the 'part-whole' relationship, giving children an understanding of grouping and regrouping strategies, which will be needed in Unit 12 for vertical addition and subtraction.

Unit 12 in *Inspire Maths* Pupil Textbook 1B connects the skills and concepts taught so far, introducing numbers up to 40. A minimum of one week is suggested to teach the place-value sequences in Unit 12 in Pupil Textbook 1B. The previous learning of numbers up to 20 and the partitioning of numbers 10 up to 20 are recapped and then built upon with the same pattern of learning, by:

- Adding and subtracting, comparing and ordering numbers to 40, with or without concrete representations, identifying patterns and relationships. Introducing children to varied representations alongside place-value charts and numerals ensures that the structure of 2-digit numbers and their place value are understood. ❶

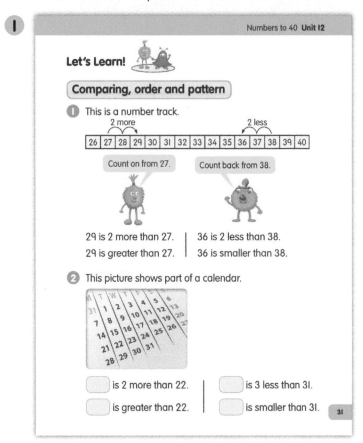

Inspire Maths Pupil Textbook 1B, page 31

At the start of Unit 17, Numbers to 100, previous learning of numbers up to 20 and the partitioning of numbers 10 up to 20, then 40, are recapped and then extended, to explore numbers up to 100. The Unit Starters and Illustrations for every unit (resources available on *Inspire Maths Online*) first recap learning, and then introduce the new unit. The mirroring of the teaching sequence and the approach, as numbers increase, allows children to focus on the continued pattern of the number system:

- Adding and subtracting, comparing and ordering numbers to 100, with or without concrete representations, identifying patterns and relationships. Introducing children to varied representations alongside place-value charts and numerals ensures that the structure of 2-digit numbers and their place value are understood.

Assessment opportunities and activities to provide deeper exploration for all can be found in the *Inspire Maths* Assessment Book 1, alongside the Put On Your Thinking Caps activities, Challenging Practice and Problem Solving opportunities in the Practice Books. ①

The first unit in *Inspire Maths* 2 is Numbers to 1000, and the pattern of teaching sequence continues as in *Inspire Maths* 1, recapping on previous learning, comparing, counting, and arranging numbers in ascending and descending order up to 1000. This logical, step-by-step teaching sequence offers clear lines of progression. You can see clearly which step of the sequence a child is struggling with, allowing effective and timely intervention and support.

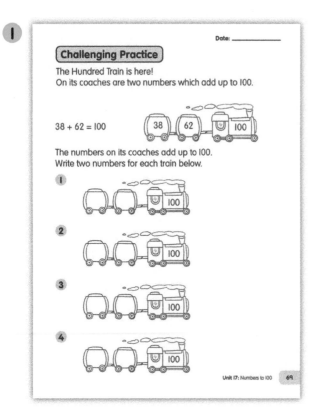

Inspire Maths Practice Book 1D, page 69

Pace and progression in *Inspire Maths* I: Money

In *Inspire Maths* IB, money is introduced in Unit 18 and continued in Unit 19.

Previous learning – Unit 18

The Unit Starter on *Inspire Maths Online* for Unit 18 shows coins and notes emptied from a money box and the teacher guidance makes connections to earlier learning of ordering numbers, counting and grouping items in Units 14 and 17. Now the grouping is of different coins and notes.

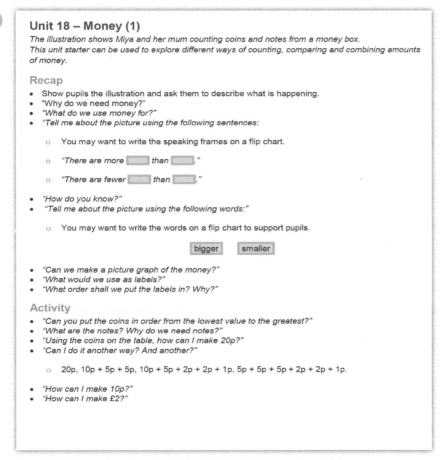

Unit 18 – Money (1)
The illustration shows Miya and her mum counting coins and notes from a money box.
This unit starter can be used to explore different ways of counting, comparing and combining amounts of money.

Recap
- Show pupils the illustration and ask them to describe what is happening.
- "Why do we need money?"
- "What do we use money for?"
- "Tell me about the picture using the following sentences:
    - You may want to write the speaking frames on a flip chart.
    - "There are more ▢▢▢ than ▢▢▢."
    - "There are fewer ▢▢▢ than ▢▢▢."
- "How do you know?"
- "Tell me about the picture using the following words:"
    - You may want to write the words on a flip chart to support pupils.

        bigger   smaller

- "Can we make a picture graph of the money?"
- "What would we use as labels?"
- "What order shall we put the labels in? Why?"

Activity
- "Can you put the coins in order from the lowest value to the greatest?"
- "What are the notes? Why do we need notes?"
- "Using the coins on the table, how can I make 20p?"
- "Can I do it another way? And another?"

    - 20p, 10p + 5p + 5p, 10p + 5p + 2p + 2p + 1p, 5p + 5p + 5p + 2p + 2p + 1p.

- "How can I make 10p?"
- "How can I make £2?"

Inspire Maths Online: Inspire Maths I Unit Starters Teacher Guidance

New learning – Unit 18

In *Inspire Maths* I, you will see that different aspects of money are explored in a logical, step-by-step approach:

- Real-life examples of using money
- Recognising coins and notes
- Writing the symbols of £ and p to record amounts of money
- Exchanging coins for notes and vice versa, for example five £1 coins = one £5 note. Children will not combine pence and pounds, for example £1·50, in *Inspire Maths* I; this step will be taught in *Inspire Maths* 2.

- Examining, classifying and comparing coins and notes
- Matching a coin or a note to an equivalent amount, using coins or notes of another denomination. This builds on previous learning about the 'part-whole', where the whole amount stays the same, while the number of parts and the amounts in the parts might change. ①

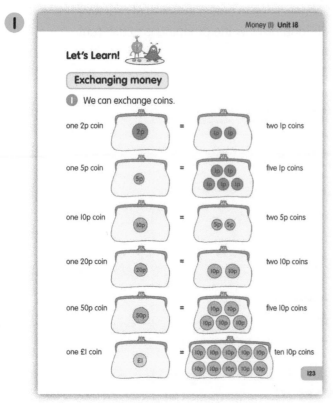

Inspire Maths Pupil Textbook 1B, page 123

Play or real money is used in all activities to ensure that procedural and conceptual understanding are integrated.

Handling money, children investigate:

- Making 100 by sorting one-pence pieces into groups of 10 and stacking the coins
- Exchanging but only to one denomination
- Counting in fives and in tens to work out an amount of money. Note you will teach this earlier, in Unit 14 – at this stage an amount is not found by multiplying, as this skill will be taught in *Inspire Maths* 2.

Vocabulary and skills from earlier units are applied to:

- Comparing amounts of money, for example, fewer, more, greater than, less than
- Using the 'counting on' strategy previously taught in *Inspire Maths* 1 to count amounts of money.

The medium-term planning recommends a minimum of one week of lessons for your teaching of Unit 18. The careful, step-by-step development of skills and understanding in Unit 18 is vital preparation for the content of Unit 19, which is covered in the following two weeks.

Previous learning – Unit 19

The Unit Starter on *Inspire Maths Online* for Unit 19 recaps on learning from the previous unit and also Unit 14: Multiplication, finding amounts by repeated addition. The starter activity provides a bank of questions to ask, exemplifying questions which could be asked for the first 'Let's Learn' teaching sequence.

Unit 19 recaps on the skills from Unit 17: Numbers to 100, where adding and subtracting of whole numbers within 100, with and without regrouping, was covered extensively.

①

> **Activity**
> * *"What coins could I use to pay for a pencil?"*
> * *"Give me another way. And another."*
> * *"What coins could I use for to pay for 2 key rings?"*
> * *"Is that the only way?"*
> * *"You have a 10p coin. What could you buy?"*
> * *"You have £1. What could you buy?"*

Inspire Maths Online: Inspire Maths 1 Unit Starters Teacher Guidance

New learning – Unit 19

The structures and strategies of addition and subtraction are very familiar to children, but here they are applied using coins. Addition and subtraction of money in multiples of fives and tens, with regrouping, is covered in the first 'Let's Learn' in Unit 19. The careful design of this lesson ensures that children's learning is not overloaded and is supported by the same mathematical structures and concepts covered in prior learning, focusing learning on:

* Using coins to add items together in pence to find a total cost

* Subtracting the total from an amount of money to calculate the change. This is the first time that the concept of 'change' is taught, as previously exact amounts were made with coins. **②**

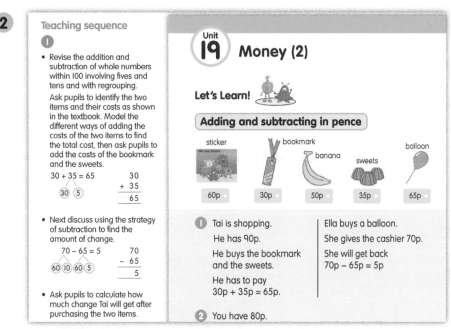

Inspire Maths Teacher's Guide 1B, page 252

Children are taught to employ different strategies taught in previous units, such as number bonds, partitioning into 'part-whole', and to evaluate these choices. This is followed by eight pages in the Practice Books.

In the next teaching sequence, children apply these skills to:

- Adding and subtracting in pounds

- Practising these skills, solving word problems, either in pence or in pounds

- Writing word problems based on money, demonstrating depth of understanding and an opportunity to assess and identify any misconceptions.

Examples of questions and activities to develop deeper understanding of money can be found on *Inspire Maths Online*: see Guidance on using Assessment Books.

> **3** Ruby has five coins in her pocket.
> The coins are 5p, 10p and 20p coins.
> The coins are worth 75p.
> What are the five coins?
> Draw the coins below.

Inspire Maths **Assessment Book 1, page 108**

Money will be revisited in *Inspire Maths* 2B, Unit 11. Previous learning will be recapped, with children handling money and identifying coins and notes. Children will learn how to state, write and read the total amount of money in pounds *and* pence, before calculating with money.

Achieving depth through careful pace and progression

This tried-and-tested authentic maths programme from Singapore facilitates mastery through its organisation of topics and its rigorous structure, based on best practice principles and methods of teaching and learning mathematics. To help your children to achieve deep conceptual understanding, the programme should be followed in the order it is presented. Adopting a 'pick and mix' approach to using the *Inspire Maths* programme is not recommended. However, there is often an overlap between Key Stage 2 and Key Stage 3 requirements, and professional judgement should be used as to whether, and when, Key Stage 2 or 3 material should be taught. As well as having a secure conceptual underpinning for successful progress through the curriculum, children also need to be developmentally ready. This is particularly crucial in relation to successful transition from concrete operational thinking (mathematical knowledge and operations linked directly to concrete concepts and examples) to more formal and abstract mathematics. When children have secure foundations, deep understanding and guided support, they can approach some of these questions with great success.

Since *Inspire Maths* is the Singapore Maths programme in its entirety, the potential of *Inspire Maths* to help children in the UK achieve mastery is immense. After many years of success in helping Singaporean children master maths, we are confident that the purposeful organisation of topics and robust approach for developing individual concepts in *Inspire Maths* will enable children in the UK to achieve similar results. High attainment and high equity are achievable when teaching is supported comprehensively by well-designed resources. Adopting a new way of teaching and learning mathematics will always be a challenge to start with, but you will be taking your first step to truly improving the teaching and learning of mathematics in your school, and increasing the understanding and enjoyment of maths for both your teachers and your children.

How to teach with *Inspire Maths*

Key features

Teaching for mastery is central to the *Inspire Maths* approach. The books are structured around a rigorous and systematic teaching pathway, which emphasises continuous, active reinforcement of concepts to ensure that children develop deep conceptual understanding. Teaching is based on the principle of children working together to develop understanding before moving on to new concepts. Assessment opportunities throughout ensure that children receive rapid, appropriate intervention, so they progress with their peers and do not fall behind. Teachers are encouraged to use careful questioning, exemplified in the Teacher's Guide, to support children who need additional help, and challenge those requiring more depth. Mathematical conversation is encouraged, ensuring that children of different abilities can support each other and enrich their understanding and vocabulary.

Inspire Maths follows the structure and progression of the curriculum in Singapore which is recognised globally as one of the most impactful ways to teach and learn mathematics. Because it follows this cumulative spiral approach, concepts and skills may be introduced in a different order to that of the 'National curriculum in England: mathematics programmes of study'. It is important that Pupil Textbooks are completed before moving on, so children build on previous knowledge and develop a deep understanding of key concepts.

Inspire Maths focuses on developing problem-solving skills, leading children to become confident and efficient problem solvers, which is critical for success at school and later in the work place. This learning framework, with problem solving at its heart, builds on the development of skills, concepts and processes alongside positive and robust attitudes and metacognition in order to achieve the core goal of deep conceptual understanding.

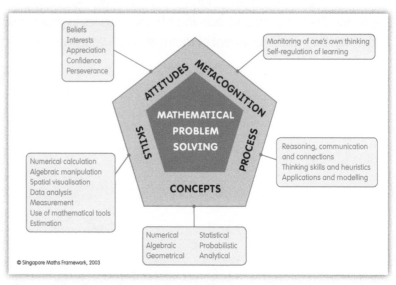

The principles that underpin *Inspire Maths*

The concrete–pictorial–abstract (CPA) approach is central to the *Inspire Maths* programme. Carefully considered and constructed representations are used in the Pupil Textbooks and Practice Books to support children's learning. These representations are excellent examples of the concrete apparatus that might support the teaching and learning. In *Inspire Maths* there is a consistent and coherent use of models and images. It is important that children develop a range of visualisations for deep conceptual understanding. You may want to introduce other manipulatives such as Numicon shapes.

The spiral curriculum and the use of variation theory ensure that concepts are frequently revisited and systematically developed to ensure fluency and deep conceptual understanding. Mathematical language is introduced progressively through the programme from the start and children are encouraged to use it in their conversations. The Teacher's Guides clearly outline the language children will be introduced to, which is highlighted in the 'Let's Learn!' sections, followed by opportunities to practise using it in questions and activities.

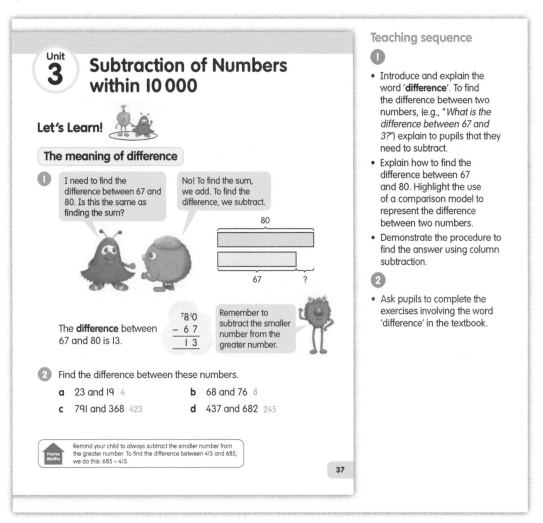

Inspire Maths Teacher's Guide 3A, page 63

The same mathematical language introduced in the Pupil Textbooks is used in the Pupil Practice Books, Assessment Books, and modelled in the teaching sequence so children have opportunities to use, clarify and practise using correct mathematical vocabulary. This supports children's deep understanding, familiarity and fluency within a concept and ultimately their confidence in mathematics.

In *Inspire Maths* there is significant focus on number and calculation. This emphasis is to ensure that these areas are taught in depth since a secure grasp of number and calculation is fundamental to understanding other areas of mathematics. These firm foundations are critical to ensuring successful progression in mathematics.

All National Curriculum objectives are covered either in the Pupil Textbooks or through additional activities available on *Inspire Maths Online* (www.oxfordowl.co.uk). You can be sure that all relevant curriculum objectives are covered by the end of each key stage in accordance with National Curriculum guidance.

Teaching with *Inspire Maths*

Importance of CPA and using manipulatives

There is growing evidence that if children have memorised and practised procedures without understanding, they may have difficulty in learning later to bring meaning to their work.[1] Many children learn and apply procedural rules without real understanding. They often forget those procedures or remember them incorrectly. To truly understand and enjoy mathematics children need to be procedurally and conceptually fluent: they need to know both 'how to' and 'why'.

Inspire Maths is based on best practice principles and methods of teaching and learning mathematics, including the CPA approach. The CPA approach is based on Bruner's conception of the enactive, iconic and symbolic modes of representation[2]. His research on the development of children looked at how children made sense of the world and focused on three models of representation of mathematical ideas. This heuristic approach has been advocated by the Ministry of Education in Singapore since the 1980s and advocates learning by doing, with the teacher guiding children through and between the three stages.

Stage 1: enactive

This stage focuses on learning through action. At this stage children are manipulating concrete materials in order to access abstract mathematical ideas and derive enactive knowledge; for example, using Numicon shapes to support children's understanding of odd

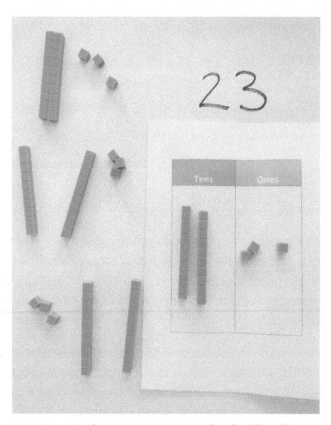

Grouping using base-ten apparatus and embedding place value

---

1 Stigler, James & Hiebert, James. (1999). *The teaching gap: Best ideas from the world's teachers for improving education in the classroom.* New York, NY: The Free Press.

2 Jerome Bruner, *The Culture of Education*, Harvard University Press, 1996.

and even numbers and base-ten apparatus to support children's understanding of groups of ten. Children can use apparatus and move it around to understand that 23 is 20 + 3 or 10 + 10 + 3 or 3 + 10 + 10.

Stage 2: iconic

This stage is about learning through image-making – often taken just to mean a visual image, but actually meaning all the senses. This includes children making their own images or drawing a pictorial representation. This is a crucial bridge to accessing and understanding formal abstract knowledge.

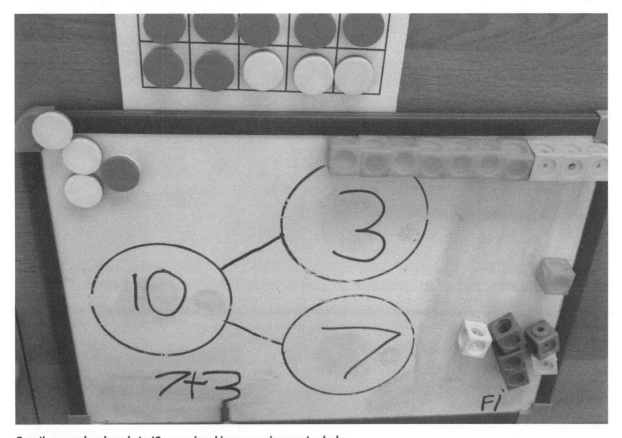

Creating number bonds to 10 as a visual image, using part-whole

Stage 3: symbolic

In this stage the learning is supported through language, both spoken and written. When children first encounter the number system they are faced with abstract symbols. As teachers we need to be mindful not to skip through to the abstract or symbolic mode too quickly.

If we move children to the symbolic, or abstract, stage before they're ready, they can start to rely on procedural rules that they use without understanding. This leads to gaps and misconceptions which can have a profound effect on their mathematical development.

Bruner suggests that learners should progress through the stages, but that the best learning takes place when all three modes of learning are used together. His research reinforces the importance of action, imagery and conversation. Bruner's three stages are made more accessible by changing the names to concrete, pictorial and abstract (CPA). It is important to remember that this is not a linear journey and that children, at all ages, will weave backwards and forwards through the CPA approach when working within a conceptual field.

Variation theory

As discussed in **High achievement in mathematics and the importance of high-quality textbooks** (on pages 18–23), textbooks are a highly structured and supportive learning tool for both teachers and learners. The principles underpinning the structure and the development of the *Inspire Maths* Pupil Textbooks are drawn from years of educational research and are proven to support the effective teaching and learning of mathematics. Dienes' theory[3] relating to the teaching and learning of mathematics specifically relates to mathematical variation and perceptual variation, or the 'multiple embodiment principle'. Dienes discussed that, to support children's concept formation and deep understanding, the concept structure should be presented in as many different perceptual variations as possible. In Singapore, educators discuss two types of variation: perceptual and mathematical. In Shanghai, educators talk about procedural and conceptual variation. Many influential mathematicians, such as Anne Watson and John Mason, continue to research the variation theory today. Mason says that variation and invariance are strongly linked since, "invariance only makes sense and is only detectable when there is variation".[4]

"Invariance in the midst of change" (Mason) means asking, "what is the same and what is different?" about, for example, a group of shapes, two or more numbers, geometrical constructions, or algebraic expressions. This encourages children to compare and contrast the structure of both, so developing deep understanding.

Mathematical variation

When referring to mathematical variation, the mathematical concept stays the same but the variation is in the maths.

In this example, children add a 2-digit number to a 1-digit number, first by adding the ones without regrouping. They progress to two 2-digit numbers, adding the tens without regrouping. They go on to adding a 2-digit number to a 2-digit number but adding the ones without regrouping. Later they will add a 2-digit number to a 1-digit number, adding the ones and regrouping. The mathematics varies in very small conceptual steps, challenging children to use their maths skills flexibly and appropriately, deepening understanding.

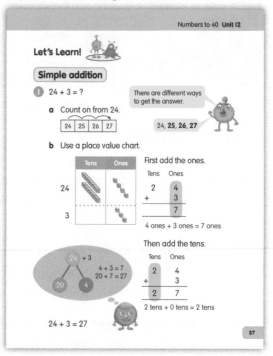

Inspire Maths Pupil Textbook 1B, page 37

---

3 Dienes, Z. (1960). Building Up Mathematics (4th edition). London: Hutchinson Educational Ltd.

4 Mason, John. (2007). Research and practice in algebra: Interwoven influences. Open University UK. P.917. Available here: https://www.researchgate.net/publication/266570395_RESEARCH_AND_PRACTICE_IN_ALGEBRA_INTERWOVEN_INFLUENCES

Perceptual variation

With perceptual variation, the mathematical concept is the same but the children are presented with different ways to perceive the mathematical ideas.

In this example, children can see 258 represented by base-ten apparatus, how this relates to the numbers and positions in the place value chart, and what the number represents in unit form, for example, 258 would be 2 hundreds 5 tens 8 ones. 258 is written in expanded form as 200 + 50 + 8, supported by base-ten apparatus and place value charts, or in abstract form as 200 + 50 + 8 = 258. **❶**

Children practise these elements on the following pages of Pupil Textbook 2A, and have opportunities for further practice and resolving errors and misconceptions in the Simmering Skills Activity on *Inspire Maths Online* (*Inspire Maths* 2, Activity 1). **❷**

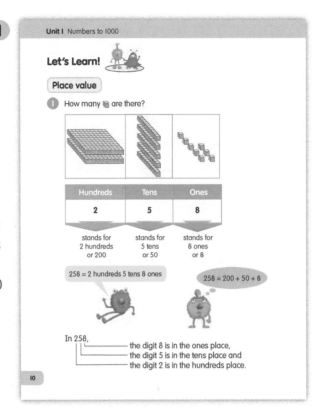

Inspire Maths Pupil Textbook 2A, page 10

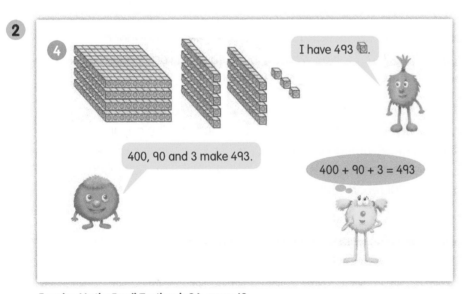

Inspire Maths Pupil Textbook 2A, page 12

Summary

Throughout *Inspire Maths* there is a consistent use of models and images using the CPA approach, and of perceptual and mathematical variation. This ensures that children are offered a variety of opportunities to develop deep understanding of mathematical structures and ideas. New concepts are introduced concretely using representations and manipulatives so that children learn through doing. These are then developed and reinforced more abstractly using the CPA approach. Alongside this there is a very careful use of perceptual and mathematical variation which builds familiarity and develops fluency. Using the CPA approach and variation theory in everyday teaching is a crucial part of supporting and developing our children's mathematical thinking and teaching for mastery.

Preparing to teach with *Inspire Maths*

Inspire Maths teaching materials are designed so that all children can progress together, introducing concepts through direct teaching to the whole class.

Working through the content with children at a pace that enables them to study concepts in depth, and progressing when the large majority have understanding, is key for developing deep conceptual understanding. Our assessment of when to move children on is then based on evidence that they are secure in the maths but have also demonstrated depth, for example, mathematical reasoning through less routine questions or problem solving in different contexts.

Children who work in mixed-ability pairs tend to make more progress, as they are all seen to have a lot to offer and a "mathematical voice". Teachers are often surprised when children who they thought were the quick graspers do not have the understanding to explain their reasoning. When working in pairs or groups children are actively learning together and supporting each other's learning, and so fostering an environment of cooperation and achievement. One school using *Inspire Maths* says how working in this way has helped with progress for all.

> "More children are working at greater depth. Children who would have been lower ability are now not labelled as such and many children have made significant progress in their year groups."
>
> Judith Myhill, St Thomas CE Primary School

If you currently arrange your children in ability groupings you may need to consider a move away from this set-up. Your children will be working in mixed-ability pairs and may not always sit with the same talk-partner or even on the same table.

There has been some research into whether children who are placed in ability sets at an early age tend to perform to the level of their teachers' expectation and the gap in ability tends to widen as they progress through their primary years.[5] The findings of the Millennium Cohort Study, a major research exercise which is following the lives of 19 000 children born in the UK in 2000–2001 reports that,

> "…streaming in primary schools would appear to increase the gap between higher- and lower-attaining pupils, and also to accentuate socio-economic differences, because more of those from poorer backgrounds tend on average to be in the lower streams."

Other considerations for setting up your classroom are whether to have a specific area for teaching the whole class (this may be a carpet area for younger years), or when you want to focus on a particular group of children (those struggling or those grasping new ideas quickly), and what maths equipment you have available. Ideally you should avoid sharing equipment with another class as different types of equipment should be available for all children all of the time, if possible on their tables or easily accessible.

---

5 http://www.cls.ioe.ac.uk/news.aspx?itemid=3064&itemTitle=Streaming+pupils+by+ability+in+primary+
school+widens+the+attainment+gap&sitesectionid=27&sitesectiontitle=News

Using the Teacher's Guides

As well as this Getting Started Guide, there are two Teacher's Guides per *Inspire Maths* level, providing planning and implementation support, and a suggested teaching sequence corresponding to each Pupil Textbook page. The Teacher's Guide gives teachers guidance on appropriate points for formative assessments throughout the teaching sequence. They are carefully designed to help teachers assess children's understanding, and their use of vocabulary and mathematical connections. The pedagogical guidance introduces the theory underpinning the approach, the features of the Pupil Textbook structure and how teachers can use them. A step-by-step teaching sequence highlights points for intervention to address gaps in understanding and opportunities for practice and enrichment through the Pupil Practice Books. The Teacher's Guide is designed for non-specialist mathematics teachers to deliver the content.

Long-term planning

Each Teacher's Guide contains long- and medium-term plans. The long-term plan gives an overview of the units and key concepts in that particular Pupil Textbook, for example, Teacher's Guide 3A outlines the units in Pupil Textbook 3A. There is also guidance for when to use the reviews and revisions in the Pupil Practice Books and the tests in the Assessment Books. The reviews, revisions and tests are usually highlighted after two units.

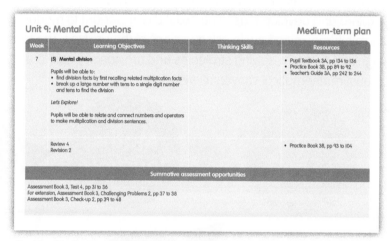

Inspire Maths Teacher's Guide 3A, page 231

Medium-term planning

The medium-term plans indicate how many weeks each section in a unit may take, together with the learning objectives, an outline of the thinking skills and Pupil Textbook resources you will need. The time given is only an indication: it is important to use your own professional judgement as to when to move your class on, being aware that some children may need extra support and further practice. The Practice Books and Assessment Books can offer valuable evidence of progression and support you in deciding when to move children on. Annotating the Teacher's Guides can create a record of how long you spent on a particular section for when that content is revisited the following year with a different class.

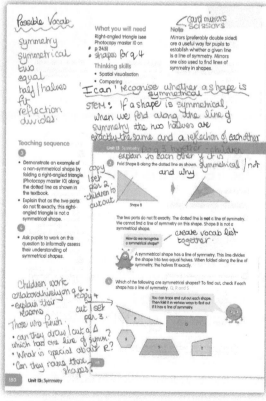

Inspire Maths Teacher's Guide 4B, page 180 (annotated)

The Teacher's Guides will give you guidance on how to get started and a suggested teaching sequence for each page of the Pupil Textbook. Make sure you are familiar with the learning objectives, key concepts, key thinking skills and problem-solving strategies you will be introducing and working on with your class. There is a suggested list of equipment to have available, which can be supplemented as necessary. Mathematical language introduced in the unit is listed and explained.

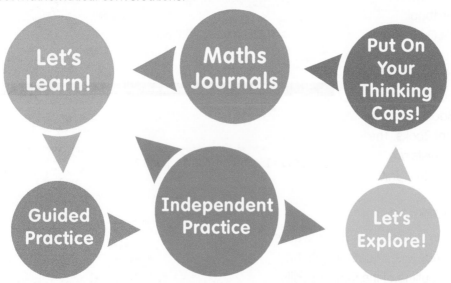

Inspire Maths Teacher's Guide 3A, page 63

The teaching sequence provides step-by-step guidance to help you meet the learning objectives with suggestions for questions to ask children. It also includes careful questioning to support the use of concrete apparatus. Opportunities for higher order questioning help children to become confident problem solvers, and encourage mathematical conversation to explore and develop reasoning skills. It is important to model higher order questioning so that children know how to ask questions of themselves. The teaching sequence will also highlight problem-solving strategies and provide support to encourage purposeful and robust mathematical conversations.

Let's Learn! → ← Maths Journals ← Put On Your Thinking Caps!

Guided Practice → Independent Practice → Let's Explore!

A suggested teaching sequence. Note that the size of each circle is not representative of the time needed for each area, as this will be guided by your professional judgement or the area of mathematics that you are working on.

Inspire Maths characters

The characters support and guide children throughout the programme from *Inspire Maths* 1 to *Inspire Maths* 6. There is a family of six characters and all of the names, Googol, Noogol, Koogol, Ooogol, Zoogol and Toogol, are variations of Googol. Googol is a very large number (10^{100} or 10 to the power of 100). The characters pop up throughout the books offering tips, hints and suggestions and demonstrate that they support each other in the same way that the children will be supported by you.

Noogol

Googol

Ooogol

Koogol

Toogol

Zoogol

'Let's Learn!' to build firm foundations

Each unit in the Pupil Textbooks starts with several 'Let's Learn!' sections to support your direct teaching. Mathematical concepts are carefully introduced in these sections. Concepts are broken down into small steps for children to follow and refer back to easily. These steps are consistently introduced using the CPA approach. As the small steps are laid out explicitly in each unit, children can refer back to previous steps when needed. When teaching from the 'Let's Learns', you will be "imparting the knowledge", as Dr Fong, the author of *Inspire Maths,* would say.

Your direct teaching will not be prescriptive in nature. Instead, you will be interacting with children and engaging them in mathematical conversations, using differentiated questions and allowing time for children to discuss their thoughts, answers and reasoning with partners, in groups or with the whole class. Listening to children's mathematical conversations, and observing their use of concrete apparatus and their approach to an activity, allows you to assess understanding.

Consider whether children will sit at tables or elsewhere, and whether they will be recording on their whiteboards or maths journals to show their thinking or answer your questions. It is good to remember that having children facing you during the lesson, by whatever means, reduces distractions and improves attention. Many teachers find that having a visualiser really supports their teaching. In addition, around a quarter of the 'Let's Learns' are also available on *Inspire Maths Online*, for use on an Interactive Whiteboard. When working through the 'Let's Learns', you will find opportunities to assess each child's understanding through listening to their mathematical conversations, observing their use of concrete apparatus and how they approach an activity.

Example

In this 'Let's Learn!' children are introduced to adding within 10, and associating adding with the part-whole and adding on concepts. The Teacher's Guide suggests that you use button magnets on a board to model counting a group of 5 then adding 2 more to the group. You may choose to use an alternative resource and to use more than one example before you introduce children to the marbles and cups as modelled within the Pupil Textbook. Remember that with the CPA approach you and the children will be using the concrete resources alongside the book illustrations. Here you will also see that the characters provide support and guidance for the children. Googol introduces the '+' symbol and the vocabulary of 'plus', 'add' and 'equals'. ❶

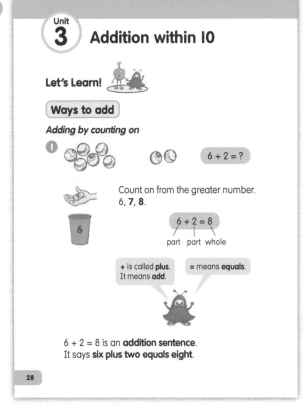

Inspire Maths Teacher's Guide IA, page 28

'Guided Practice' to develop deep understanding

After a concept has been introduced in the 'Let's Learn!', guided and collaborative practice develops the deep understanding required for mastery. 'Guided Practices' are indicated by empty answer boxes or the 'Activity' subheading. The Teacher's Guide offers support in questioning and guiding children's understanding of the concept, encouraging interaction between children and with you. It is important to remember that these empty boxes do not mean "fill in the answer". Children work collaboratively, in pairs or small groups, to develop their mathematical language and reasoning.

You can guide those who need support to think of other ways to get to the answer and also probe for common misconceptions. Encourage children to explore using different manipulatives, observing how they use the concrete apparatus and listening to their mathematical conversations. Whilst children are working through the 'Guided Practice' and activity questions you will have the opportunity to continue to assess: which children require further support, which need to consolidate their learning, and which will need to go deeper with further challenge.

Example

In the 'Let's Learn!' that precedes this guided and collaborative practice, children have been introduced to the terms 'greater than', 'smaller than', 'greatest', 'smallest', 'more than' and 'fewer than' to compare and order numbers to 20. Remember that with the CPA approach you and the children will be using the concrete resources alongside the book illustrations, focusing on comparing numbers and arranging in ascending and descending order. The Teacher's Guide suggests that children use a set of cubes to support them to create the different sets to be compared. You may also choose for them to use straws as they could begin to bundle them into tens and ones. Children will be asked to discuss the questions and explain their answers to each other and to the whole class. ❶

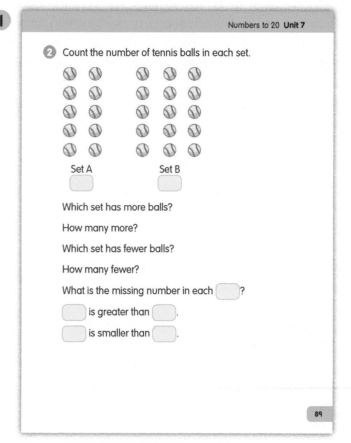

Inspire Maths **Pupil Textbook 1A, page 89**

'Let's Explore!' and 'Games' to investigate and apply learning

In the Pupil Textbooks, engaging 'Games' (*Inspire Maths* 1–4 only) and investigative 'Let's Explore!' activities encourage children to apply concepts they have been learning and to practise applying their learning further by working collaboratively in small groups, in pairs or individually. Children will be exploring concepts whilst providing teachers with an opportunity to assess their reasoning skills by observing how they approach the tasks. The 'Let's Explore!' activities and 'Games' have been carefully designed to support children with frequent opportunities to develop deeper understanding, to make connections through mathematical reasoning and to engage in mathematical conversations using precise vocabulary.

Example

Prior to this 'Let's Explore!' children have been using concrete representations to show the concept of division as finding the number of equal groups. They have developed the strategy of distributing objects equally in each group. Through this activity they will explore the different numbers of groups they can make with the twenty-four cubes. As a paired activity, children will check that each group has an equal number of cubes. You could extend the activity by asking children to present their findings either pictorially or abstractly. ❶

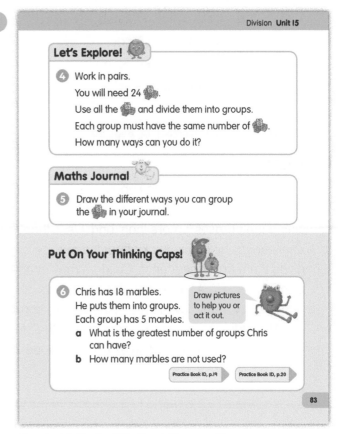

Inspire Maths Pupil Textbook 1B, page 83

'Maths Journals' to reflect

The 'Maths Journal' is where each child records their mathematical thinking and reflects on their learning. A typical 'Maths Journal' would be a child's own exercise book. The 'Maths Journal' activities are designed to support children to reflect upon their learning. They also develop into a valuable assessment tool that will show progress over time. They create an opportunity for children to share their thinking and progress and help to establish a sense of pride in their achievements. In this book they can also record their thoughts, ideas, findings and their response to the activities they complete in other sections of the Pupil Textbook.

> ### Maths Journal
>
> Which of these sentences are correct?
> a   A bicycle has 2 wheels.
> b   A triangle has 3 sides.
> c   7 is smaller than 5.
> d   8 is 1 less than 9.

Inspire Maths **Pupil Textbook 1A, page 20**

Example

Here, children have been using cubes and a range of other concrete resources working with numbers to ten. They have also experienced using and interpreting statements containing the phrases '1 more than' and '1 less than' a given number. This 'Maths Journal' task challenges children to think about the number of objects in a real-life scenario alongside the number sequence. Children may need to be encouraged to think about questions such as 'Are there enough cups or enough biscuits?', 'How many people could sit down?', 'How many flowers are in the vase?', and so on. As this activity is in Unit 1 you may scribe children's reflective responses and their thinking for them and make a note in their 'Maths Journal' of the resources used to support their reflections.

'Put On Your Thinking Caps!' to challenge

The 'Put On Your Thinking Caps!' activity often appears at the end of a unit and challenges children to solve non-routine problems. These activities have been designed to enable children to draw on prior knowledge as well as newly learnt concepts. To complete these, children will need to use problem-solving strategies and critical thinking skills such as comparing and sequencing. They are also valuable for assessment to determine whether a child has developed a deep understanding of a concept either through their oral or written explanation, their concrete modelling or their pictorial representations. Children who grasp a concept more quickly than their peers may access these questions earlier, but it is essential that all children are given the opportunity to be challenged and assessed for mathematical fluency and greater depth of understanding.

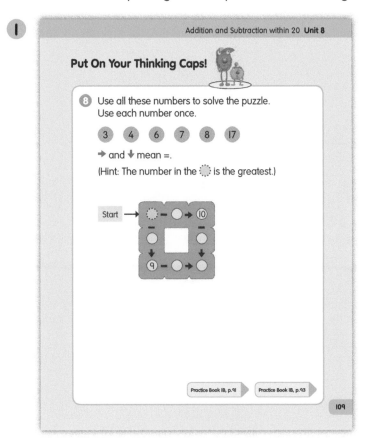

Inspire Maths Pupil Textbook IA, page 109

Example

This 'Put On Your Thinking Caps!' activity concludes children's study of addition and subtraction within 20. During this unit children have used the 'make 10' and the 'regrouping into tens and ones' strategies to solve various calculations. They have accessed various concrete resources and used pictorial representations alongside abstract number sentences. This activity requires children to allocate each number given to an empty circle in the squares, ending up with the number in the bottom right hand square no matter which route is taken. Look for children who quickly identify that 17 is the largest number and therefore will be located in the orange circle at the start. As 9 and 10 are provided as the difference between two unknowns and 17, children should apply their number bonds to quickly complete this part of the puzzle. Some children may need apparatus such as Numicon shapes or numeral cards to enable them to quickly shuffle through the options. ❶

'Home Maths' to encourage mathematical conversations

Throughout the Pupil Textbooks there are 'Home Maths' activities for you to use. These suggestions are for parents and carers to work through with their children, so that they can explore maths further outside the classroom, engage in mathematical conversations and develop a home-school partnership. Any equipment required should be available in the home. Further home activities with guidance for parents, such as questions to ask and what to look and listen for, are available on *Inspire Maths Online*. These are a powerful way to involve parents and carers in their children's mathematical learning. They also help children to see maths in the world around them.

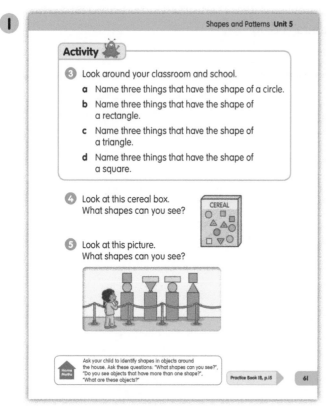

Inspire Maths Pupil Textbook 1A, page 61

Example

This 'Home Maths' activity follows on from the children identifying shapes in real-life objects and also in illustrations. ❶

Practice Books to develop fluency and consolidate

Practice Books are an essential component of *Inspire Maths* and of any mastery programme. They contain a wealth of activities and questions to develop confident and fluent mathematicians who are working towards a deep conceptual understanding. The questions are carefully constructed to reinforce children's understanding and provide varied and frequent practice. Independent practice and consolidation are essential and integral parts of the mastery approach. Practice Books also give you the valuable opportunity to consider each individual child's progress. Each child will complete all or selected elements of the books, as you direct. There are four Practice Books each for *Inspire Maths* 1–3 and two Practice Books each for *Inspire Maths* 4–6.

Guidance on when to use the Practice Books can be found in the Pupil Textbooks and in the Teacher's Guides. Some units have a few pages of content before linking to the Practice Books. However, there should be daily opportunities for independent practice: investigating or reasoning with manipulatives; playing games or engaging in mathematical conversations.

There are various activity types in the Practice Books. Each unit begins with well-structured questions within the 'Practice' section. These help children to consolidate the key concepts from the Pupil Textbook. They are to be completed independently and often feature guidance from the characters to support children. You may choose to annotate children's Practice Books to record whether concrete resources, and which ones, have been used to support their thinking.

After the 'Practice' sections have consolidated the learning, children are provided with 'Challenging Practice' and 'Problem Solving' questions. These questions use new and different contexts, providing opportunities for critical thinking and mathematical reasoning to develop fluency and deepen understanding. The 'Problem Solving' questions are often word problems and may require children to draw representations of their thinking. The regular reviews help children to reinforce and consolidate learning and build understanding. The 'Revisions', which appear at the end of the corresponding Pupil Textbooks, draw from a range of preceding topics, concepts and strands for complete consolidation of each Pupil Textbook. The final type of activity within the Practice Books is the 'Maths Journal', where children showcase their understanding of the concepts covered by creating their own questions or statements to explain their mathematical thinking.

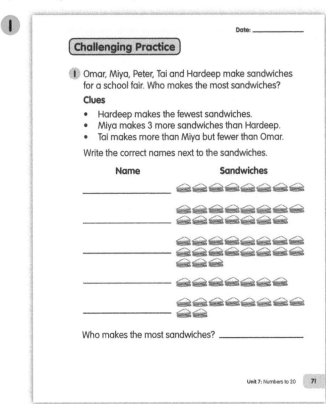

Inspire Maths **Practice Book 1B, page 71**

Example

This question follows on from the 'Put On Your Thinking Caps!' activity in the Pupil Textbook which uses the thinking skills of deduction and comparing and the strategy of guessing and checking. ❶

Assessment Books to create a record of progress

The Assessment Books can be used for both formative and summative assessment, covering the key learning objectives from the Pupil Textbook. There are four check-ups for each set of Pupil Textbooks which revisit the previous units and provide opportunities to check children's understanding and monitor their progress over these units. The assessments use unfamiliar contexts so children can apply their understanding to challenging questions. You should not expect all children to be able to tackle all the questions.

Ideally, each child should be able to keep their Assessment Book throughout their school career. Remember that, for example, *Inspire Maths* 1 isn't only for Year 1, and some questions could be useful in Years 2 or 3. The questions in the Assessment Books range from the straightforward to ones which focus on depth and reasoning, and are therefore still challenging for older children. The questions can also be used for establishing and evidencing progress and assessment for teaching and intervention.

Assessment Book content can be used as tests at the end of units of work, or as a resource to build your own sets of questions. You may also choose to use some for further challenge or as a homework activity. You can set questions as a 'cold assessment' to assess knowledge before you teach a unit and again as a 'hot assessment' after teaching to check understanding and show evidence of progress.

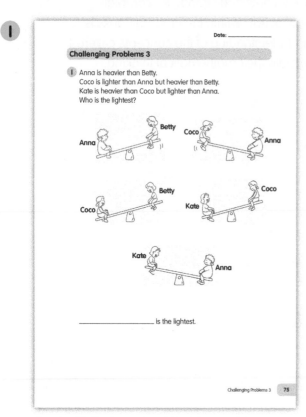

Inspire Maths **Assessment Book 1, page 75**

Example

There are four units that follow the unit on mass before this 'Challenging Problem' is advised to be completed. Children may use just the written clues and/or pictures to reason the solution. You may want to extend the question by asking children to design their own questions linked to this problem, for example, 'Can you explain why that particular child is the lightest?', 'Who is the heaviest and why?'.

Challenging practice

Although your quick graspers will be working on the same area of mathematics as the rest of the class, you will want to know how to keep them enthusiastic, challenged and engaged. It is important not to accelerate children through the material as a means of challenging quick graspers, as grasping a concept quickly doesn't always mean that it is understood deeply or secure for the future. The *Inspire Maths* approach challenges quick graspers to deepen their understanding, rather than moving them on too quickly. The many opportunities for challenge include: 'Challenging Practice' and 'Put On Your Thinking Caps!' sections; challenging problems throughout the Pupil Textbooks; Assessment Book questions; and teacher questioning.

Consider whether your quick graspers can represent the problem you have given them in a variety of ways, using different types of concrete apparatus. Can they show you using a pictorial method, or using abstract symbols and methods? Ask questions to encourage children to identify patterns and structures, for example, 'What if you are working on 9 + 3 and bridging 10?' See which children apply the "make 10" strategy and if they apply this in various addition situations such as 8 + 4, 7 + 5, 6 + 6, etc. This will deepen understanding of adding two 1-digit numbers, grouping in tens, and consolidating number bonds to 10. It will start to build the deep understanding of place value crucial for later mathematical concepts.

Think about asking questions to encourage children to identify patterns and structures, such as, 'Can you explain how you worked it out?', 'How could you do it differently?', 'How could you check your answer?', 'Can you show me using different apparatus?', 'Can you make up a question to go with this number sentence?'.

There are lots of open-ended and challenging questions in the *Inspire Maths* Practice Books and Assessment Books to use as a springboard for deeper questioning, for example, 'Still using the numbers 1–6, can you make a different total so that all the numbers along each side add up to the same number?', 'What about replacing the numbers 1–6 with the first six even numbers?', 'What totals can you make?', 'Can you make these totals in different ways?', 'Can you make an odd total? Why?'. ①

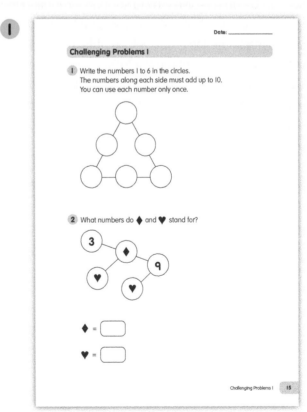

Inspire Maths Assessment Book 1, page 15

Struggling learners

At the beginning of Year I some children may find reading the content challenging. Your use of words and concepts in your teaching is central to children's reading of the Pupil Textbook. Indeed, some schools have reported that *Inspire Maths* supports their reading progress. You could pre-read the page to children so that they are not encountering unfamiliar words in the lesson, or consider pairing struggling children with fluent readers to support them.

Prepare by looking in the Teacher's Guide at the 'Key Concepts' and words children will be using. You will also find a word list on *Inspire Maths Online.* Pre-teaching these words and phrases, for example, by using flashcards, will help children who find reading more challenging.

Younger children will also need direct teaching to physically use the Pupil Textbook, for example, locating particular pages. Children usually pick this up amazingly quickly and enjoy using their Pupil Textbooks. If you have a visualiser, you can use this to show children the page they are looking for and to explain the structure of the Pupil Textbook, for example, contents page, page numbers, colours and characters. You will find further support on *Inspire Maths Online* for introducing children to the *Inspire Maths* Pupil Textbooks and Practice Books.

There will always be children who struggle to understand a particular concept, and it is our responsibility to recognise and support these children in their learning journey. Assessment throughout the teaching pathway ensures that children can receive rapid, appropriate intervention when they need it, and before they fall behind. Same day intervention is now seen to be an effective way to support struggling learners' understanding and fill in gaps. Irrespective of ability, all children should be part of your direct teaching, and will be working on the same topic. You will be able to address their different needs through your questioning and the use of manipulatives you encourage them to use. Differentiation is a challenge for all teachers and we recognise that traditional methods have put a limit on children's learning. We need to aim for effective differentiation and challenge for all children.

Introducing *Inspire Maths* in your school

If your school starts using *Inspire Maths* part-way through a school year, or if older children start using it for the first time, you will need to familiarise them with the Pupil Textbooks and the approach: using manipulatives; engaging in mathematical conversations; explaining their reasoning; and working as a whole class as well as with partners. You will need to ensure that children are ready to start working on the Pupil Textbooks, being mindful that Year 2 children may be working on *Inspire Maths* I.

As with introducing any new programme, you will need to assess children's understanding of key topics, establishing and evidencing what they do and do not understand. It's important to ascertain your starting point carefully, to ensure that you don't miss anything out, or overlook misconceptions or gaps in children's understanding. You could use the 'End of Year Assessments' on *Inspire Maths Online* to help you do this, for example, use the Year I 'End of Year Assessment' to identify gaps in your Year 2 children's understanding.

Use the 'Transition Guides' and the 'Overview of Units' on *Inspire Maths Online* to identify what prior knowledge children need to access the learning. The 'Transition Guides' provide detailed information of where to look in earlier units. Remember that the *Inspire Maths* textbook numbering may not be the same as school year groups. You might need to use *Inspire Maths* I with your Year 2 children, and that's fine.

Some schools implementing *Inspire Maths* have restructured their curriculum by splitting the maths lesson into two daily sessions. Direct teaching and guided practice generally take place in the first session, with structured intervention in the second. Time between the two gives teachers the opportunity to consider how they will manage the second session. In these schools, the second session generally comprises three elements: further support and practice for struggling learners; support and challenge for consolidation and challenging questions; and practice for greater depth.

> The *Inspire Maths* programme has given me the confidence and the staff the confidence to make the best judgement that we can for our children so they develop the love of learning for mathematics. That confidence is going to take them forward to make sure that they have the very best start at Primary school.
>
> Jackie Savage, Outwood Primary Academy Lofthouse Gate

In the next section you will be able to read how *Inspire Maths* meets age-related expectations in the National Curriculum.

How does *Inspire Maths* relate to the National Curriculum?

Introduction

Inspire Maths is the UK edition of the Singaporean textbook programme *My Pals are Here!*, used by Singapore children since 2001 and currently adopted by 80% of Singapore schools. *My Pals are Here!* follows the Singapore curriculum, a spiral curriculum that continually builds and consolidates knowledge to provide deep understanding. The spiral curriculum and progression of concepts within *My Pals are Here!* has been trialled and revised extensively over the last 17 years, and the results speak for themselves. Singapore schools consistently rank at the top of international performance studies, including the Trends in International Mathematics and Science Study (TIMSS 2015) and the Programme for International Student Assessment (PISA 2015).[1] The effects of the *My Pals Are Here!* programme in raising standards of teaching and learning have also been felt in the UK, as shown in a significant independent study on the impact of *Inspire Maths* in UK schools,[2] as well as through the rise of Advocate Schools across the UK who report on how their teaching and learning has been transformed.[3] The continued success of the Singapore curriculum, as well as the extensive content-development process behind *My Pals are Here!*, demonstrate why *Inspire Maths* faithfully maintains the structure and progression of the original Singapore *My Pals are Here!* programme.

Maintaining the conceptual progression and development of topics in *Inspire Maths* is also important in light of their academic foundations. The *Inspire Maths* programme is firmly underpinned by the work of internationally-renowned educationalists, as detailed in the **Pace, progression and fidelity** section of this Guide. Of particular note is Skemp's theory that learning mathematics by relating ideas to each other (relational understanding) is more meaningful, and therefore more effective, than memorising facts and procedures (instrumental learning).[4] Skemp's ideas about relational understanding are central to the organisation of the units in *Inspire Maths*, which is designed to help children make connections across topics and thus deepen their conceptual understanding. The integrity of progression in *Inspire Maths*, which is not only research-based but proven to work in practice, is therefore essential to retain.

---

1 http://www.oecd.org/pisa/pisa-2015-results-in-focus.pdf

2 Hall J., Lindorff A. and Sammons P., Evaluation of the Impact and Implementation of Inspire Maths in Year 1 Classrooms in England; Findings from a Mixed-Method Randomised Control Trial. (Oxford: Department of Education, University of Oxford, 2016): https://ore.exeter.ac.uk/repository/handle/10871/24265

3 For more information, see **'Proof of impact and research base'** pp. 10–17.

4 Skemp, Richard R., Relational Understanding and Instrumental Understanding (Warwick: Department of Education, University of Warwick, 1976): https://www.atm.org.uk/write/MediaUploads/Resources/Richard_Skemp.pdf

As we have discussed, *Inspire Maths* follows the Singapore curriculum as developed in the *My Pals are Here!* programme. That said, there are many similarities between the Singapore curriculum and the 2014 'National curriculum in England: mathematics programmes of study'. Firstly, the 2014 National Curriculum is fundamentally based on the curriculum of countries such as Singapore, as detailed by the NCETM:

> "The content and principles underpinning the 2014 mathematics curriculum reflect those found in high performing education systems internationally, particularly those of east and south-east Asian countries such as Singapore, Japan, South Korea and China."[5]

A key aspect of this influence is reflected in the adoption of a mastery approach to learning maths. The 2014 National Curriculum in England, as in Singapore, is a mastery curriculum. A mastery curriculum is designed in relatively small sequenced steps, which should each be mastered before children move to the next step. In addition, the introduction to the National Curriculum states: "Mathematics is an interconnected subject in which pupils need to be able to move fluently between representations of mathematical ideas."[6] This acknowledges the ideas of educationalists such as Skemp which, as we have seen, are a fundamental underpinning of *My Pals are Here!* and consequently of *Inspire Maths*.

Furthermore, the 2014 National Curriculum aims for all children to be mathematically fluent, to be able to reason and to solve problems. These aims are reflected in the *Inspire Maths* core principles, encouraging children's 'confidence', 'reasoning', 'thinking skills' and 'problem solving', as shown in the diagram below.

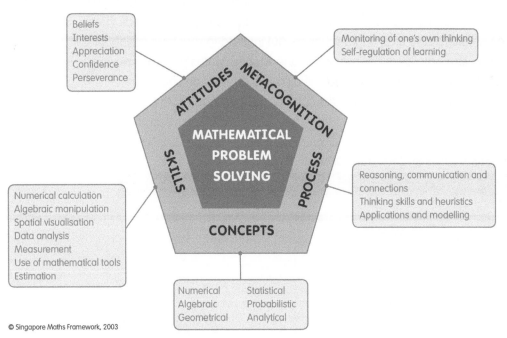

© Singapore Maths Framework, 2003

The principles that underpin *Inspire Maths*

As illustrated, both the Singapore and English national curricula are rooted in the same core principles, making the *Inspire Maths* programme a trusted and proven resource to improve teaching and learning in the UK classroom.

---

5 NCETM, Mastery approaches to mathematics and the new National Curriculum, Oct 2014: https://www.ncetm.org.uk/public/files/19990433/Developing_mastery_in_mathematics_october_2014.pdf

6 Department for Education, National curriculum in England: mathematics programmes of study (2014): https://www.gov.uk/government/publications/national-curriculum-in-england-mathematics-programmes-of-study

As *Inspire Maths* follows the cumulative, spiral approach of the Singapore curriculum, concepts and skills may be introduced in a different order to that of the 2014 National Curriculum in England. The progression of the units in *Inspire Maths* textbooks enables children to access content in the order that has proven to be successful over decades in Singapore. Equally, the numbering of *Inspire Maths* textbooks is not directly related to UK school year groups or National Curriculum coverage; *Inspire Maths* is structured by stage rather than by age. For example, it is not necessary to cover all the content in *Inspire Maths* 1 in Year 1. Children can continue working on *Inspire Maths* 1 in Year 2, as it is important that all children have a secure and deep understanding before moving on to the next stage. This is outlined further in the **Pace, progression and fidelity** section of this Guide.

Whilst there are differences in the ordering of topics between the Singapore and English national curricula, in following the *Inspire Maths* programme you can be confident that all relevant curriculum objectives will be covered by the end of each Key Stage. There is plenty of support and guidance on *Inspire Maths Online* (www.oxfordowl.co.uk) that will help you ensure you have met the requirements of the 2014 National Curriculum, and this support is outlined on the following pages.

Supporting resources

National Curriculum Correlation Charts

There are detailed correlation charts provided on *Inspire Maths Online* that show where the National Curriculum concepts for each year group are taught and practised in *Inspire Maths*, including references to the specific units and sections in the Pupil Textbooks. These are not intended as an alternative teaching sequence, but instead to reassure schools that all National Curriculum objectives are met within the *Inspire Maths* programme and demonstrate where they can be found. You will also find correlation charts on *Inspire Maths Online* to show how *Inspire Maths* can be mapped against the Curriculum for Wales.

Inspire Maths 1 National Curriculum Correlation Chart

Year 1 programme of study Statutory requirements	*Inspire Maths* Pupil Textbooks 1A and 1B	Notes
Number – number and place value		
Pupils should be taught to:		
• count to and across 100, forwards and backwards, beginning with 0 or 1, or from any given number	PB1A Unit 1: Numbers to 10, 6–21 PB1A Unit 3: Addition within 10, 28–31 PB1A Unit 4: Subtraction within 10, 39–43 PB1A Unit 6: Ordinal Numbers, 67–79 PB1A Unit 7: Numbers to 20, 79–97 PB1B Unit 12: Numbers to 40, 26–62 PB1B Unit 17: Numbers to 100, 91–120 PB2A Unit 1: Numbers to 1000, 6	Counting across 100 is included in *Inspire Maths* 2.
• count, read and write numbers to 100 in numerals	PB1A Unit 1: Numbers to 10, 6–12, 15–21 PB1A Unit 2: Number Bonds, 22–27 PB1A Unit 3: Addition within 10, 28–38 PB1A Unit 4: Subtraction within 10, 39–53 PB1A Unit 7: Numbers to 20, 79–97 PB1B Unit 12: Numbers to 40, 26–62 PB1B Unit 17: Numbers to 100, 91–120	
• count in multiples of twos, fives and tens	PB1A Unit 7: Numbers to 20, 95, 97 PB1B Unit 12: Numbers to 40, 36 PB1B Unit 17: Numbers to 100, 91–93	*Inspire Maths* 1 introduces number patterns. 'Skip-counting' for twos, fives and tens is introduced in *Inspire Maths* 2.
• given a number, identify one more and one less	PB1A Unit 1: Numbers to 10, 17–20 PB1A Unit 7: Numbers to 20, 94–96 PB1B Unit 12: Numbers to 40, 36	
• identify and represent numbers using objects and pictorial representations including the number line	PB1A Unit 1: Numbers to 10, 6–21 PB1A Unit 2: Number Bonds, 22–27 PB1A Unit 3: Addition within 10, 28–30, 32–37 PB1A Unit 4: Subtraction within 10, 39–51 PB1A Unit 7: Numbers to 20, 79–97 PB1B Unit 12: Numbers to 40, 26–61 PB1B Unit 17: Numbers to 100, 91–100, 102–117	*Inspire Maths* uses number tracks frequently. Use number lines as an alternative image alongside number tracks, for example in PB1A Unit 1: Numbers to 10, page 12 and PB1A Unit 7: Numbers to 20, page 82.

Inspire Maths 1 · National Curriculum Correlation Chart

Inspire Maths Online: **Year 1 National Curriculum Correlation**

For *Inspire Maths* 2 onwards, the National Curriculum Correlation Charts also indicate where there are additional activities online to support full curriculum coverage.

Additional activities

The additional activities on *Inspire Maths Online* are designed to be used alongside the *Inspire Maths* Pupil Textbooks to ensure full coverage of the National Curriculum. In an instance where a National Curriculum objective is not covered within the *Inspire Maths* textbooks, it is always covered within the additional activities online. The additional activities can be integrated into an *Inspire Maths* teaching sequence at the beginning or end of a lesson, introduced through a daily 'Maths meeting' or taught through other areas of the curriculum such as Science, P.E. or Art.

Key Stage expectations

There is some content within *Inspire Maths* 2 that goes beyond Key Stage 1, as well as some content within *Inspire Maths* 6 that goes beyond Key Stage 2. While the *Inspire Maths* programme is aspirational, there is no expectation that you teach beyond the National Curriculum expectations for your Key Stage, unless you are confident that the necessary Key Stage content has been consolidated and children are secure with deep conceptual understanding. As well as having a secure conceptual underpinning for successful progress through the curriculum, children also need to be developmentally ready. This is particularly crucial in relation to successful transition from concrete operational thinking to more formal and abstract mathematics. However, if children have secure foundations, deep understanding and guided support, they can often approach some of this content with great success. Bar models are also widely used in *Inspire Maths* to help children visualise, reason, problem solve and access more challenging problems. There are detailed charts at the end of *Getting Started Guide* 2 and 6 that can help you identify the National Curriculum Key Stage objectives that each *Inspire Maths* unit maps onto.

Assessment support and national tests

We recommend that children's progress is tracked through the *Inspire Maths* resources, including the assessment books, which map onto the cumulative, spiral curriculum adhered to by the *Inspire Maths* programme. However, schools may also wish to track children's progress against National Curriculum expectations. To support this, we have produced three additional assessments for each year group, which are designed to be used at the start, middle and end of the school year. These assessments, along with supporting mark schemes and tracking spreadsheets, can be found on *Inspire Maths Online*. They have been written in the style of the National Curriculum tests, and map onto National Curriculum objectives, so that you can be sure your children are on track and are well-prepared for their Key Stage 1 and 2 assessments.

Inspire Maths equips children with the deep conceptual understanding, fluency, reasoning and problem-solving skills they need to be successful in their national tests. On the following page you can see some examples of questions from the 2017 Key Stage 2 SATs papers,[7] alongside pages from the *Inspire Maths* Pupil Textbooks that illustrate how using *Inspire Maths* will help your children to prepare for their formal assessments.

---

7 The full Key stage 2 test papers: 2017 mathematics test materials are available here: https://www.gov.uk/government/publications/key-stage-2-tests-2017-mathematics-test-materials

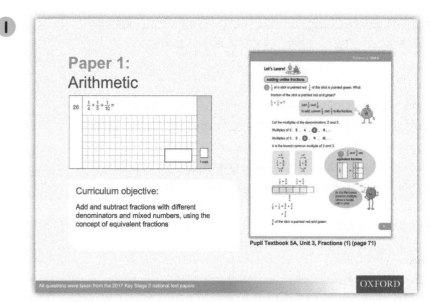

Inspire Maths and the Key Stage 2 national test papers

In this example from the Key Stage 2 arithmetic paper, children are asked to add together three fractions with different denominators. This concept is taught in *Inspire Maths* 5A, where children learn how to add unlike fractions with the use of supporting models.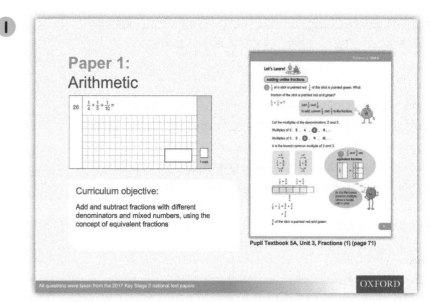

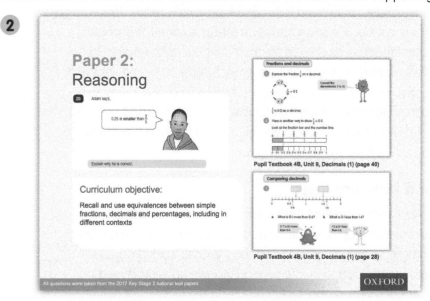

Inspire Maths and the Key Stage 2 national test papers

In this example from the Key Stage 2 reasoning paper, children are asked to compare a decimal to a fraction. This curriculum objective is taught in *Inspire Maths* 4B, in which children learn multiple methods to convert fractions to decimals and are then taught to compare decimals with the support of a number line.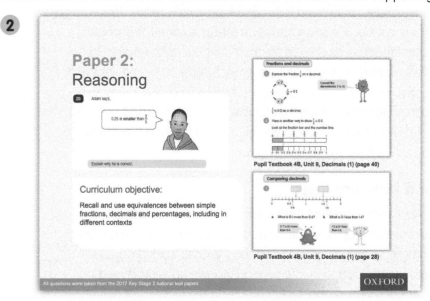

If you are teaching in Year 2 or in Year 6, the 'Year 2 and Year 6 National Curriculum tests (SATs) guidance' document on *Inspire Maths Online* provides alternative teaching sequences for these year groups to ensure your children meet the end of Key Stage National Curriculum objectives ahead of their national tests, whilst maintaining the proven progression of topics in *Inspire Maths*.

How does Inspire Maths relate to the National Curriculum?

Using the supporting resources for *Inspire Maths* I

On the following pages you will find examples of the supporting National Curriculum resources for *Inspire Maths* I, including the unit progression, additional teaching opportunities and the assessment support to ensure full National Curriculum coverage for your year group.

Inspire Maths I

We recommend starting *Inspire Maths* I in Year I and following the sequence of units within the textbooks in order to deliver the full aims of the *Inspire Maths* programme. The following tables detail the unit progression from *Inspire Maths* Pupil Textbooks IA and IB, alongside notes on additional teaching opportunities. Similar information is available in the '*Inspire Maths* I National

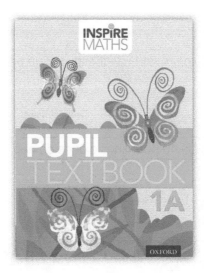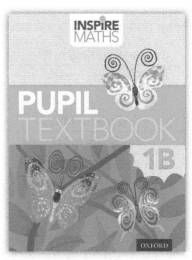

Curriculum Correlation' chart on *Inspire Maths Online*. There are no National Curriculum Additional Activities for *Inspire Maths* I, as the elements of the Year I National Curriculum that are not covered in *Inspire Maths* I are covered in *Inspire Maths* 2 and therefore before the end of Key Stage I. Instead, we have included notes on 'additional teaching opportunities'. These are supporting notes based on the National Curriculum objectives for Year I to keep in mind as you teach the content within the related unit.

Unit	Title	Additional teaching opportunities
	Inspire Maths IA • Practice Books IA and IB • Assessment Book I	
I	Numbers to 10	Use number lines alongside number tracks. Explore and use the language of 'equal to, most and fewer'.
2	Number Bonds	
3	Addition within 10	Explore and use the language of 'not equal to'.
4	Subtraction within 10	
5	Shapes and Patterns	
6	Ordinal numbers	
7	Numbers to 20	Use number lines alongside number tracks.
8	Addition and Subtraction within 20	
9	Length	

Unit	Title	Additional teaching opportunities
	Inspire Maths IB • Practice Books IC and ID • Assessment Book I	
10	Mass	
11	Picture Graphs	
12	Numbers to 40	
13	Mental Calculations	
14	Multiplication	
15	Division	
16	Time	Explore and use the language associated with time and times of the day, including 'earlier, later, quicker and slower'. Find opportunities to explore sequencing and the language of days of the week, weeks, months and years. Also include activities that include children drawing the hands on clock faces.
17	Numbers to 100	
18	Money (I)	
19	Money (2)	

For reference, areas of the Year I National Curriculum that are developed in *Inspire Maths* 2 are as follows:

- Counting across 100 is covered in *Inspire Maths* 2, Unit I.
- Skip-counting for twos, fives and tens is introduced in *Inspire Maths* 2, Units 5 and 6.
- Half and quarter of an object or shape is covered in *Inspire Maths* 2, Unit 12.
- Time taken and elapsed time is covered in *Inspire Maths* 2, Unit 13.
- 3D shapes are introduced in *Inspire Maths* 2, Unit 17.

How does Inspire Maths relate to the National Curriculum?

Using additional teaching opportunities and assessments in practice

Following the teaching sequence in *Inspire Maths* IA Unit I, you will come to teach 'Numbers to I0' in the autumn term. You can see from the unit progression table on the preceding page that there are two additional teaching opportunities to go with this unit. Let's take, for example ,"Explore and use the language of 'equal to', 'most' and 'fewer'". When working with children on the 'Let's Learn!' on page I3, which covers comparison and related mathematical language, it would be a good opportunity to ensure children are confident using the terms 'equal to', 'most' and 'fewer', first by modelling them and then by encouraging children to use them throughout the activities that follow. ●

You can now be confident that children have accessed this National Curriculum objective before you return to teach the rest of Unit I in the Pupil Textbook, which will consolidate and deepen this understanding. As you progress through *Inspire Maths* I, you can use the unit progression table on the preceding page to see when to intertwine the other additional teaching opportunities into your teaching.

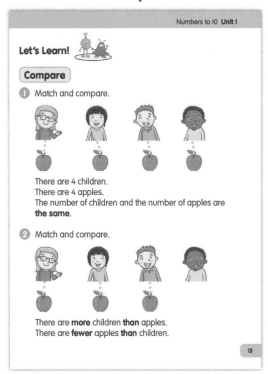

Inspire Maths Pupil Textbook IA, page I3

Throughout the year, you can also use the Beginning, Middle and End of Year Assessments for Year 1 on *Inspire Maths Online*, and the accompanying mark books, to track children's progress against Year 1 National Curriculum objectives. We have provided both arithmetic and reasoning papers to ensure that children become familiar with the style of questions they will encounter in their national assessments. The Year 1 assessment papers are shorter than those in the other year groups as children will be less familiar with formal assessments.

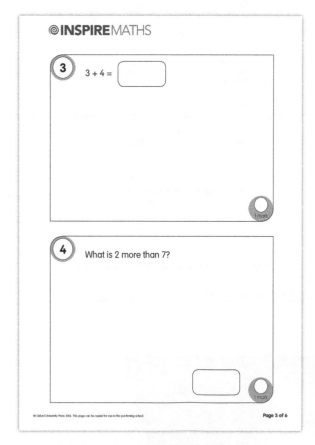

Inspire Maths Online: Beginning of Year Assessment
Year 1 Paper 1: Arithmetic, page 3

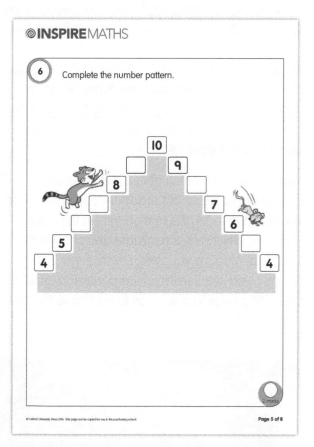

Inspire Maths Online: Beginning of Year Assessment
Year 1 Paper 2: Reasoning, page 5

Summary

Using the *Inspire Maths* textbook programme, children can be taught together and progress together. Singapore's experience and the experience of *Inspire Maths* schools in the UK show that high attainment and high equity are achievable when teaching is supported comprehensively by well-designed resources. Most importantly, following the programme fully will ensure that all National Curriculum objectives are covered. While the *Inspire Maths* curriculum is aspirational, there is no expectation that you teach beyond the National Curriculum expectations of Key Stage 2, unless you are completely confident that your children are secure with deep conceptual understanding and are ready for these next steps. *Inspire Maths* is a proven, high quality maths curriculum based on years of research and refinement and provides a secure foundation for our children to become confident learners, proficient problem solvers and capable mathematicians.

The next and final section in this Getting Started Guide details further support for successful implementation. This crucial support to improve the teaching and learning of mathematics in all situations is available on *Inspire Maths Online*.

Further support for successful implementation

Inspire Maths Online (www.oxfordowl.co.uk) contains a wealth of additional resources to help schools effectively implement the *Inspire Maths* programme. No two schools are the same, and so this bank of resources has been created to meet the needs of teaching *Inspire Maths* in your particular classroom. Some of the resources are introduced below. Lots more can be found on *Inspire Maths Online*.

Planning

Digital and editable copies of the medium- and long-term plans from your Teacher's Guides can be found online, detailing the progression of the units in the textbooks, plus a breakdown of the key concepts within each unit. These will help you to plan your own timetable, as well as giving an overview of what has been or will be taught in other year groups, so that you understand the overall progression of the programme. The long-term plans will offer suggestions of where you might use the tests, challenging problems and check-ups from each Assessment Book as well as the Practice Book reviews and revisions. The medium-term plans give you more detail on what you will be teaching, the learning objectives, the thinking skills and suggested resources required. In schools where there is more than one teacher per year group, the plans help to provide valuable consistency across teaching.

Teaching

Mixed-age classes

Adopting a mastery approach in a mixed-age class is a challenge faced by many teachers, especially those in smaller schools. 'Planning for a Mixed-Age Class using *Inspire Maths*' on *Inspire Maths Online* comprises practical considerations, long-term planning support, sample weekly plans and an editable weekly planning template to help teachers adapt their teaching for more than one year group. There are various options open to you when using *Inspire Maths* in a mixed-age class; for example, you may ask a Teaching Assistant to take one of the year groups while you take the other, or you may teach the same lesson to your whole class, with the older children working in greater depth. Most importantly, the plans suggest how to order the units in the *Inspire Maths* books to maintain the spiral progression while keeping similar areas of mathematics together for consistency of teaching and management of concrete resources.

To see this in practice, the 'Managing Mixed-Age Classes' video and 'Teaching *Inspire Maths* in Mixed-Age Classes' case study show how teachers at St Mark's C.E. Primary School successfully teach mixed-age classes using the *Inspire Maths* programme.

Mixed-ability classes

The mastery approach requires all children to be working on the same concept in the lesson. *Inspire Maths* supports schools by providing resources to teach concepts at a variety of depths, allowing teachers to cater for the range of different abilities in their classroom. A sample of these tools is outlined below.

Quick graspers

The *Inspire Maths* Assessment Books are a great resource for formative and summative assessment. 'Getting the most out of the *Inspire Maths* Assessment Books' provides teachers with guidance on how to extend these assessment questions to provide greater depth and challenge in the classroom, including 30 examples across all six *Inspire Maths* Assessment Books. These examples give quick graspers the opportunity to reflect, discuss and investigate independently.

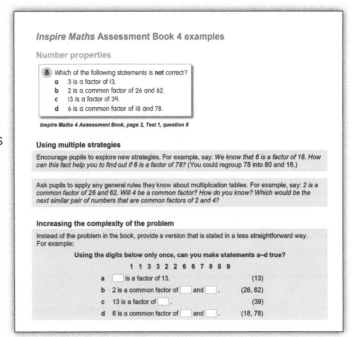

Inspire Maths Online: Getting the most out of the *Inspire Maths* Assessment Books, p.21

Simmering Skills

'Simmering Skills' are designed to give teachers extra support in teaching essential number skills that underpin children's mathematical understanding and confidence and keep them bubbling away throughout the year. The 'Simmering Skills' activities comprise PowerPoint slides and accompanying teachers' notes to use in class, which together provide extra support for teaching key areas such as number, place value and fractions. They are also a useful tool for struggling learners, as earlier 'Simmering Skills' activities can be revisited to support gaps in knowledge and understanding.

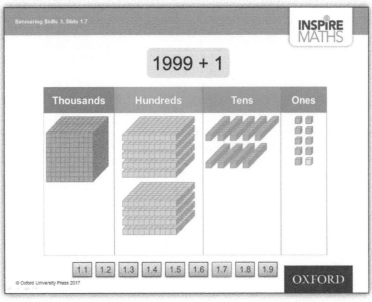

Inspire Maths Online: *Inspire Maths* 3 Simmering Skills, Activity 1, Slide 7

The 'Case Study 2: Managing Mixed Ability Classes' video and accompanying teacher handout shows how teachers at Hayfield Lane Primary School cater for their mixed-ability classes using the *Inspire Maths* programme.

> *Inspire Maths* supports teaching in mixed-ability groups because it enables children to have those mathematical conversations, develop that mathematical language that we know is a key part of learning; it helps them to clarify their thinking and extend their learning.
>
> Liz Ryland, Hayfield Lane Primary School

Implementation in later years

The 'Transition Guides' are designed for teachers of classes from Years 2 to 5 who are new to *Inspire Maths*, to use in the first seven weeks of the academic year. For example, as a teacher introducing *Inspire Maths* 2 to your class for the first time, you will need to teach essential content from *Inspire Maths* Textbook IA and IB so that children have the required knowledge and skills to access the content in *Inspire Maths* 2. The seven-week transition content, plus the content within *Inspire Maths* 2A and 2B, can all be completed in one academic year.

Inspire Maths 5 Transition Overview

Week by Week

Inspire Maths 5 Week 1	Day 1	Day 2	Day 3	Day 4	Day 5
Essential reading	Teacher's Guide 4A	Teacher's Guide 4A	Teacher's Guide 4A	Teacher's Guide 4A	Teacher's Guide 4A
Unit	Unit 1	Unit 1	Unit 2	Unit 2	Unit 2
Pages (TG4A)	Pages 2 – 17	Pages 2 – 17	Pages 24 – 50	Pages 24 – 50	Pages 24 – 50
Main teaching points *You will need plenty of equipment, such as Dienes apparatus, straws, Numicon Shapes, etc. for work on factors.*	**Pupil Textbook 4A Numbers to 100 000** (TG4A pages 4 – 10) Count in thousands using place value counters by placing them in the thousands column as you count. When practising counting in even steps with pupils, remember to count backwards as well as forwards.	**Pupil Textbook 4A Comparing numbers within 100 000** (TG4A pages 11 – 15) Compare numbers by looking at the values in each column. Build numbers using concrete materials. Practise putting numbers in size order.	**Pupil Textbook 4A Rounding numbers to the nearest 10** (TG4A pages 28 – 32) **Rounding numbers to the nearest 100** (TG4A pages 33 – 37) Using place value knowledge, practise rounding numbers to the nearest 10 and 100.	**Pupil Textbook 4A Estimation** (TG4A pages 38 – 41) Use the rounding strategy from the previous day to round a two- or three-digit number. Use place value dice to generate different two- and three-digit numbers for pupils to round. Show how an estimate can be produced by calculating quickly in this way.	**Pupil Textbook 4A Factors** (TG4A pages 42 – 46) Introduction of factors and products. Give opportunities for lots of practice with hands on apparatus such as Cuisenaire and Numicon Shapes. Ask pupils to build 12 then rebuild it using only 2s, then 3s etc.

Inspire Maths Online: Inspire Maths 5 Transition Guide, p.4

Assessment

The Beginning-, Middle- and End-of-Year 'Assessment Papers' on *Inspire Maths Online* can also be used to inform the transition plan for the next school year. For example, you could use the End-of-Year Assessment Papers for Year 1 at the end of the summer term of Year 1, to ascertain any topics that require initial teaching, re-teaching or consolidation, and to help planning for the transition to Year 2. Mark Schemes and Markbooks will support you with your assessments.

These online assessments can help you to measure children's progress against the requirements of the 'National curriculum in England: mathematics programmes of study'. The tests have been written to align with age-related expectations for each school year, and will help children become familiar with reading and answering SATs-style questions.

Professional development

There is a range of professional development videos, including our 'Recommendations for Implementation' video and teacher handout, on *Inspire Maths Online*.

We recommend five days of professional development that has been designed for you and your school, over the first year and beyond. This includes building confidence in teaching for mastery through detailed understanding of the Singapore approach, building subject knowledge, and advice and support from expert educational consultants on planning, reviewing and reflecting on implementation.

Videos

There are lots of videos available to support your teaching and pedagogy, including what a successful *Inspire Maths* lesson might look like in the classroom, teaching for mastery and frequently asked questions. There are also accompanying handouts which summarise the key points of the videos, and which can be used for reference or to support you when planning staff meetings or parents' information evenings.

Inspire Maths Online **is updated regularly to respond to schools' requirements, so please do revisit the site for any additional support you may need when implementing and delivering the programme.**